LETTERS

TO

AND

FROM

ETERNITY

Jeff Gaura

Letters To and From Eternity

Trilogy Christian Publishers
A Wholly Owned Subsidary of Trinity Broadcasting Network
2442 Michelle Drive, Tustin, CA 92780

Cover Illustrations by: McKenna Kirkpatrick

For information about special discounts for bulk purchases, please contact Trilogy Christian Publishing.

Manufactured in the United States of America
10 9 8 7 6 5 4 3 2 1
Library of Congress Cataloging-in-Publication Data is available.

ISBN: 978-1-63769-782-5
E-ISBN: 978-1-63769-783-2

TABLE OF CONTENTS

FOREWORD

Jesus, why am I still here? The answer to this question defines the contents of this book.

On April 11, 2020, I should have died. The fireman on the scene who retrieved what was left of my bicycle verified that. The doctor who looked at my blown lung, seven broken ribs, and A/C joint verified it as well. A trip back to the crash site at the first anniversary of "life number two" convinced my wife as well.

I was at peace as I contemplated the end of my days as my bike and I flew off a CCC era bridge near the Blue Ridge Parkway and down towards the riverbed below. During the brief time I was airborne, I concluded that if my life story was to end and my gravestone declared that I lived only fifty-four years, I was okay. I had a great life. I was ready to meet my Maker.

My wife tells a different story. She says that my angel was working overtime on some last-minute messaging because God told him that it was not my time. That story you will find at the start of the book.

Laying in a hospital bed for a well-conditioned athlete and contemplative author is intimidating. But my thoughts took me away from my circumstance like a bubble bath does at the end of a day. I was rich and had reached nearly every goal that I had ever set. My bucket list had more lines in it of checked-off accomplishments than outstanding dreams. Yet, I was compelled to address the impending nature of eternity. My wife's opinion was judged to be right; for reasons that I will perhaps never know, it was not my time.

However, I complicated the process with old habits. I am a trained physicist. I built and sold a trendy business and made lots of money. I am a successful athlete. Yet none of those achievements orient my soul to look at eternity. After a thoughtful analysis, I drew my first conclusion. I needed to get up early each day, when no one would interrupt me, with the purpose of reading and writing. My new working hours were 3 a.m. to 6 a.m. Mid-afternoon naps would now be a requirement as I caught back up in the missed slumber.

More than five hundred days removed from that wreck, I look into the mirror and see a different Jeff. I am a published author many times over. I have returned to riding my bike at breakneck speeds and competing, but I will never forget what that crash did to my view of self and the world. Getting the nerve to get back on a bicycle wreck that should have killed me was convincing. Anything is possible with enough nerve, with a sprinkling of hard work to cover up the taste of a lack of confidence.

In this book, I decided to make this work as accurate as possible, which required a lot of risk and transparency. To that point, most stories in this book depict real people and real accounts with potentially unreal outcomes. However, since the conversations with eternity occur in all the stories, they all have a fictional component meant to make you think. Perhaps that is what gives their tales meaning. Maybe that is why I got so angry and cried so many times as I wrote this.

Starting on day two in the trauma ward, the only thing I thought about was people. I did the most thoughtful and prayerful analysis of literally everyone with whom I had a relationship. My heart was filled, and it was broken repeatedly. I had invested my time and my money in many people, and there were many glorious outcomes. Yet, there were some tragedies that I had used busyness to avoid, and it hurt me to relive my role in the failures. Between bouts of reliving my wreck, these poor outcomes pressed me to answer one of life's biggest questions.

What happens when we die?

That question elicits answers just like the ones you would receive if you asked a stranger, "How long is a piece of string?" The secular world creates visuals of clouds, harps, and arguably immense intervals of boredom. Others visualize an instantaneous transfer to New Jerusalem with the River of Life, an orchard of the sort we cannot imagine, rapid restoration of all things, immediate and complete healing, and revelation of all mysteries. The words Elohim gave us to build a model and set of expectations are incomplete at best. Sure, heaven is described with some details, but all of the timelines and sequences for its appearance do not include "bottom of the seventh inning with two outs" sorts of descriptions.

I have decided that we are going into eternity with a faith that God knows what is best and that He will honor His promises. That said, we will debate what those promises look like while we are here. Until then, though, we all share freedom with imagination.

I used to think that we lived in a relationship from the cradle to the grave. I found that this assumption was incorrect. Our relationships extend to eternity, and this place we call earth is our practice field. If you remember one of these stories and repeat your recollection of it to someone else, then they have done their job. Each story is written in the language of the speaker. It does not represent my language as an author as much as it reflects the culture in which all of them lived and operated. As we all struggle with God, we become transparent at every level. These characters are no exception.

God can and does turn atrocities into beauty in ways that none can understand, especially me.

September 12, 2021
Monroe, NC

Are you the person I intended you to be?

-God

CHAPTER 1

My Story

"Jesus."

What else more was there to say? Every one of my senses told me that I was down to only a few cycles of brain waves before making the transition into the next realm. For God, He sees both the physical and the spiritual realities as one. For those of us living in human bodies, heaven and earth are pretty different. I was about to die, and this wasn't a scripted conversation.

Calling on the name of my Savior at the time of death was logical to me. Some material-world-only people think my all-out faith that Christ's claim to be the Son of God is intellectually immature. They think I cut the scientist's side of my being short with my agreement to this claim. I love science, but its observation methods and extrapolations don't answer life's real issues about what is real and what comes after this life ends.

That all said, I do love science. The scientist in me read the literature regarding the brain's natural preparation techniques when it signals that the body is suddenly about to die. The body releases acetylcholine. It readies the body and mind for whatever is next that doesn't include being alive, so I suspected that it was the presence of that natural agent that prevented me from hearing the roar of the river as I fell toward it.

"Jesus," I repeated His name.

My senses were prepped for the pending impact as I continued the free-fall off the bridge. My hope at the end of this fall would be to join Him not long after impact. Soon, I would get many questions answered that my scientific mind and my spiritual being have pondered for a long time. *Soon* meant *in the next few seconds.*

Hollywood has made more than one story about people flying off of a bridge in an attempt to end their lives. The difference here was that I was *not* trying to end my life, yet I was flying off a bridge, nonetheless. I entered a sharp turn on my bicycle going too fast, and I hit the old stone barricade, going rear wheel over the front wheel, and I somersaulted towards the riverbed below the bridge. My shoes were attached to my bike's pedals, and I gripped the frame as hard as possible. My hope in eternity lay in Jesus, but on earth, my scientific brain knew that there was a chance that my bike's carbon frame would absorb the impact. I played both of the odds. I gripped the bike and prayed.

"Jesus."

He teaches that when we call on His name, He will be there. The same cannot be said about my bike manufacturer. There was no need to yell out, "Cervelo."

I began the second mid-air summersault gripping my bike. My hope of a safe landing was diminishing. I had gone way too far already. I did not have E.T.-like power to right the cycle and fly into the sky. This must be it.

"I'm ready," I said, speaking out loud. God is always next to me, and He knows my thoughts, but I wanted Him to hear me. Just in case.

I was reminded that I had a great life. I retired young, and many friends have described my post-CEO existence as "the best life." I worked a day or so per week to pay the day-to-day bills, and I had made enough money from the sale of my business that I didn't even need to do that if I didn't want to. I had started on some of my lifetime bucket list items, but some of my efforts were half-hearted. I still had an unfinished book and had started athletic coaching and leading adventure travel, but I indeed wasn't focused on either of those things. I told myself that once I sold the "distraction" that an American small business creates, I would have no more excuses not to focus on the things I loved.

Nearly six months had elapsed since the sale and removing the distraction didn't help. I was still half invested in my own dreams. I didn't want to end all things with regrets.

There were good thoughts as well. My kids appeared to be well-adjusted. They figured out that going all-in with their spouse was a big part of being a victorious warrior, and they didn't get duped into playing the "wait till the right person comes along" game that their peers seem to find compelling.

My wife had everything she needed and wanted, and she loved the people all around her. She had a granddaughter and several dear friends that were a part of country living. I had a ministry that I created and led, and it had already built four schools in the Himalaya. I had peace knowing that if I were not here, all of those people and things would continue without me. My life was not a series of monuments to my work and my ego that litter the landscape of the American small business owner.

Yet how did I get to where I was flying off the edge of a bridge? I started this morning early, driving to the Blue Ridge Parkway with my bike and bike rack. I parked at the bottom of a valley and decided to pedal to the crest of the parkway and get in sixty miles of fitness challenging climbing and descending, and if weather permitted, see the views into the surrounding valleys of springtime. I expected to have the parkway to myself, and my assumptions were proven right. Usually, I would see a couple of people cycling the parkway on a Saturday morning, but there were none today. Fear of COVID had people hiding from creation as much it did keep them away from one another. I had repeatedly thanked Jesus for the day, and I also thanked him that my fifty-three-year-old body was strong and fit enough to fly up and down the mountains on my bike. I misjudged how fast I could travel and still make a turn as I crossed a bridge. I had done this turn at least four times in the past, but this one was about to be my last.

"It is well with my soul," came from my heart but without the words. I knew that I could not possibly fall this far and safely land. I was ready to meet my Maker.

That is when I saw the white hand. It appeared in front of me as I somersaulted, and it turned in the air with me. I knew a river existed below the bridge, but I didn't hear any sound of flowing water striking the rocks. I blamed it now on the white hand and not the acetylcholine.

The hand was huge, bigger than me or my bike. It wasn't trying to stop me. The craziest part about the hand was that it was covered in lists. Seeing lists on a big white hand was at least as crazy and unlikely as watching a world-class cyclist fly off a bridge because he was traveling too fast.

The lists covered the hand and were legible even though I rotated at a dizzying pace. *How is it possible that I could read them?* I need strong glasses to read, and I was certainly not wearing any.

There was a list of girls that I had slept with. Next to it was a list of all the guys I had played sports with. Seeing those two lists side by side made sense, as I met many girls playing sports, and the only guys I ever talked to about sleeping with different women were the guys I played sports with. Those lists belonged together.

There was a list of all the people I served with as an altar boy in the Catholic Church when I was eight to twelve years old. I hadn't thought about even one of those kids since I moved away from there in 1977. Nothing was next to that list other than a few single names of people I met in Nepal who talked to me about Hinduism. That was an interesting pairing. I wondered why I was seeing them now.

There were some recent lists that I also didn't know I accumulated. For example, the hand had a list of all the women I had ever taken a Pilates class with. I looked at the list and laughed. It dawned on me that men didn't do Pilates. Next to the Pilates list was a list of all the people who worked for me; ironically, this was the first time I saw that this was a primarily men's list. I tried to rationalize how I had one list of nearly all women and another list of almost all men that could be next to each other. *Was this a cultural outcome beyond my control or a moment of subconscious discrimination?*

There were some lists that I had always assumed that only God was keeping. There was a list of all the people I had prayed with, and there was a lettering scale to go along with it. However, I didn't know what the lettering meant, as it wasn't graded from A to F as our education system does. Next to the prayer list was a list of all the people I had canceled, and it was longer than I thought it would be. *What was the pattern of these lists?* Again, I wondered why those two were next to each other.

There was a list of all the people who had come to our home for a party at one time or another. That list was, by far, the biggest one. I took a moment to take some pride in that list. It was part of a more extensive list of all the people I had poured time and money into. Who would have known that all that guidance I gave people when I was a business leader and minister would be deemed as an investment during my last breaths?

I hypothesized that these lists would be a part of judgment day. Since heaven seemed to be my next stop, I wondered if the hand was part of the judgment. *The Bible never talked about a hand, did it?*

In the center of the palm was the list of all the people that I had ever told a lie to. I hated seeing how extensive that list was. It took up so much space that I felt shame. I told myself that many of those little fibs were protective lies; I didn't want to stir something up or hurt someone's feelings. *Why were those people on the same list of people I used to lie to when I told them I was an author?*

The big white hand hadn't talked, and it reminded me of Thing from the *Addams Family*. Perhaps it could answer my questions, considering how little time I had left to ask them.

"What list should I be looking at?" I asked.

"You need to look at your relationships and judge your behavior. After all, that is what He will do."

"Do I need to look at all these lists or just a few of them?" I asked.

I got no answer. Since my sense of time was gone, and the impact was imminent, I knew that any of these words might be my last. Sure enough, my intuition was correct for the second time that day, and impact happened.

In the next moment, the front wheel of my bike hit the ground first. In a flash, my chest hit the handlebars, and a shooting pain unlike any I have ever experienced went from my chest up into my face. I felt bones break over the right side of my chest and experienced what seemed like an internal balloon pop as my right lung exploded, pushing the air into my body cavity. I opened my mouth and saw stars.

The front forks holding the front tire cracked from the force of the impact as the carbon bent and then splintered. Then, something crazier than flying off of a bridge and seeing a big white hand happened. It was even crazier than seeing all those lists.

I stood up.

Science held up its end of the bargain. Sure, my bike was destroyed, and all my broken bones in my chest and shoulder were part of a newly created disaster zone, but I was standing with a crumpled bike frame between my legs. My bike's frame had absorbed much of the impact, and my legs and arms were unscathed. Even my helmet stayed on.

"Wow."

Instead of pearly gates and the first meeting with eternity, I found myself on the edge of a cold, flowing river with a stone bridge built in the 1930s over my head. I stepped over what was left of my bike with my right foot and stood on solid ground, allowing the shards of the bike to fall over. I reached with my left hand to touch the right side of my chest, and I could feel the damage. There were lumps where there should be none. I tried to raise my right hand, but the damage was too extensive, and I could not do it.

I knew from First Aid as a boy scout that I would soon head into shock from the cortisol pouring into my system, and I needed to get help. There was no cell service on this part of the Blue Ridge Parkway system, and no one knew exactly where I was. When you tell someone you are going on a sixty-mile bike ride, there is no sense of exact location. The white hand was long gone, but my science-trained mind was alive and well.

Move. I needed to move.

I knew I had to climb up and out of the riverbed and get help. I needed to get back to the highway above me. I had two working legs and one usable arm. I used to teach people that three working limbs are all they need to climb up and repel down a mountain, even a steep one; time to practice what I teach.

I scrambled up the north side of the ravine and worked my way to the side of the road and back onto the bridge. I paused to look up over the edge and down into the basin below to see where I traveled. I could only shake my head in disbelief that I was just down there. Later, the fireman who retrieved my bicycle told me that I fell thirty-one vertical feet before hitting the ground.

Shock began to set in. I laid down next to the road so anyone driving by could see me, and I waited for help. A guy named Gary stopped, and he started the rescue process. It wasn't long before I was in an ambulance racing towards the hospital. The first hospital took a lot of images. They concluded that they didn't have the resources to address the internal damage, but they charged me a lot of money to put me back in the same ambulance and send me to the next hospital with good wishes and the hope of good luck. Most of the journey from hospital to hospital was a blur, but I remember when the morphine started to work and the pain went away.

There was an exception. The white hand reappeared, but this time, it was with me on the ambulance ride to the second hospital. The sirens in the truck were blaring as my breathing was labored and unstable. The battle between the core strength in my diaphragm was pitted against a blown-up lung that was filling with fluid. Yet the hand could communicate with me.

"This doesn't seem like what I expected heaven to be," I shared as I fought to speak with only one lung in a usable state. *The ambulance driver wouldn't have the sirens blaring if I were dead, would he?*

"It isn't. You are in between where you were and there. You can't stay here, and God wants your input before He decides which way you should go," said a voice that sounded like the hand.

"What does that mean? Why does He need my input?" I asked.

"He doesn't *need* your input. He is God. He *wants* it."

The voice continued as I pondered the depth of that claim.

"Your angel protected you, and he did so upon God's request. However, you are not as helpful to the kingdom as He wants you to be, and He wants to hear from you before He chooses where you go next. Free will never dies, even in this nether space."

How is it that I am not as helpful as He wants me to be? I had never considered that perspective.

"What sort of opinion does He want from me? I mean, I want to go to heaven, but as you guys showed me, I have some damaged relationships that I would like to address. That is what you showed me with all those lists, right?"

"Lists? No, that wasn't me."

Oh, really? Who the hell was it then?

That is what I thought, but I dare not ask. This hand is obviously speaking directly to God. The hand spoke again in a repetitive tone.

"He wants your answer."

I needed to pause. I flashed back to the lists.

"I want to stay," I said.

"So be it," he said.

The hand was gone, and I saw everything you would expect to see in a hospital trauma room. There were flashing lights, beeping sounds, and people walking around wearing protective gear. Many were staring at screens and discussing my tests results. I wasn't drunk or on drugs, and they wondered how I was still breathing.

"Well, I am glad you want to stay. In fact, you are staying right here, Mr. Trauma Patient One," said the doctor standing next to me. His lab coat and tablet computer gave his role in this drama. He must have heard me talking to the hand.

"Hi, I am Dr. Brown. I am one of many who wonder how you are still alive! The ambulance drivers found no ID on you, but they have retrieved many dead bodies from motorcyclists that fell off that bridge. So let's start with your name. What is it?" he said.

After some exchanges, he held my forearm and looked me in the eye. He was trying to make a point.

"It is amazing that you are speaking, considering that you broke all but one rib and your right shoulder. You also have a pneumothorax on your right side. A pneumothorax means your lung had ruptured due to the force of the impact on your chest, and the strength of that darn core of yours allowed you to hold your breath when you landed. The air had nowhere to go, so your lung ripped from the ribcage and burst like a balloon. The air took its equivalent of a road trip and entered your chest cavity. Soon it will move upward and into your face, and you will look like the Michelin man. Don't worry; it will pass."

Great. I would soon look like the people whom I ridiculed for being out of shape and overweight. The strength of my core was to blame. You have got to be kidding me. I wanted to blame Jill and Laura, my Pilates instructors, but they didn't make me fly off the bridge.

Jeff Gaura

They both convinced me that a strong core was a good thing. This time, it wasn't. I guess what comes around goes around.

"I will see you later this afternoon. For now, though, you will need respiratory therapy every few hours to prevent pneumonia in that lung. That means you will get your sleep interrupted a lot. Let me apologize in advance for waking you through the night for a couple of days. For now, though, get some rest. Nothing speeds recovery like the body's natural methods," he said, then he left.

Early the following day, the other attending physician working that weekend came into my room, carrying a chart.

"Hello, Trauma Patient Number One! My name is Attending Physician Number Two. Nice to meet you!" he said.

I already liked this guy. After some pleasantries and more question-and-answer sessions, he shared that he was an avid cyclist, and he knew the road and bridge I wrecked on. He knew I had been here long enough to think about what happened.

"So you have been given a second chance in life. Have you been giving that much thought?"

"Some," I said.

I laughed. I just added to the hand's list of lies I told.

I should have said, "That is the only thing that occupies my mind."

I could see that God was starting the process of remaking me. He was giving me a second chance. My starting point was my old life. Everything straight ahead was my new one. *How was I going to differentiate the two? Maybe stop lying?*

There weren't that many people in the hospital, as COVID had canceled all elective surgeries. The guy named Physician Number Two had no one else to see other than a drunk driver who killed someone and was now handcuffed to his bed, so we struck up a conversation. I told him how I had recently sold my business and sorted out which relationships would carry from my old professional world to my new one. There was some heartbreak and some absolute joy as well as I started my life over. I told him about the white hand and all the lists. He admitted that he had some lists that he wished he didn't.

"So what are you going to do now? You aren't going to ride that broken bicycle all day long, are you?" he asked.

"I don't know," I said.

That was another lie. Add Attending Physician Number Two to the list of people I have lied to. *So much for change.*

The truth was I knew exactly what I would do. Second chances happen for a reason. I had my phone with me, and I had already looked at the data from the wreck. It took two point three seconds for me to go from thirty-three miles per hour when my wheels impacted the side of the bridge and decelerated to zero. That was all God needed to work. I need to be more helpful to Him; time for change number one. Tell the truth. I opened my mouth and gave it a try.

"I do know. I will write books and prove to my eighth-grade English teacher that she was wrong when she said my storytelling skills are poor. I am going to write about people on those lists I was telling you about. Hopefully, I will get an opportunity to fix them. Who knows? Gotta try, right?"

The doctor broke eye contact and prepared to stand up. He was getting uncomfortable with an unexpected exposure to lists that could have been his. He had nowhere else to go, but he didn't want to sit with me as my discomfort exposed his. I can't blame him.

My wife came to pick me up four days later, and I decided that I needed to be nice to her. Usually, I was an awful patient with no sense of patience. I had to sleep on a recliner for a few weeks since getting up and down from bed was too painful, even with the meds. I went out of my way to be kind, which was a challenge more than I led on it was.

However, as soon as I could go up and down the stairs, I sat down in front of my keyboard and looked for that old folder called "book one." Inside was a couple of lame stabs at a book. I put some work into it a few months before selling my business, and it was shoddy work. Even the outline was embarrassing. *Was my eighth-grade English teacher on to something?*

I needed a new routine, and I needed God. My efforts to create a better world weren't in line with God's idea. I knew I was meant to write. Yet, there was this issue of the lists that I could not forget.

Plan A. Write every day. Write and read your work out loud to someone. Write and pray about it. Just write. Make it a habit, as you used with drinking and learning subject matter. Make it a habit like riding a bicycle.

Plan A and a half. Pray for the people on those lists. Make things right, except when to do so would injure them or others. Maybe my writing will do that? Who knows?

Plan B. Get back on your bike. You love running, cycling, hiking, and all that goes with it. It is my identity, and God didn't take it from me. I can still do this, and I don't want my previous experience on a bicycle to be my last one.

SOMETIME LATER

Last July, about three months after my wreck, I competed in a Gran Fondo bike race in Asheville, near the Blue Ridge Parkway. I got second place overall. The guy ahead of me was about thirty years younger than me, and the guy behind me happened to be my son. God never seems to finish clarifying how far he mutates the word *crazy* and makes it into something new.

My second book is now for sale in multiple venues, and on-line retailers are selling out. My third and final book in my first trilogy is in the publisher's hands, and I have already approved the cover art and the content changes. It shall be released in time for the Christmas season. People are reading my work, and they love it. Take that, Ms. Parrot!

I love 3 a.m. now. I cry a lot. I dance sometimes. I have four monitors, and I wish I had five as I look things up and let my fingers find words to match the ideas that pour from my spirit.

I got this idea about writing a book about others who danced on the edge of eternity. *What might they learn? Who might they meet? What would be their takeaway?* I decided to write a series of letters, both to them and from them, who had stories like mine.

I got the message. I am stronger now because I was weak. I am wiser with my time because I've been foolish with it.

Lastly, I have been praying for everyone on the lists the hand showed me. There remains some unfinished business there. My faith is stronger than ever. I need only bring the shovel. God will move the mountain.

CHAPTER 2

This letter was based on Kristen's earth event but continued as a fictitious eternal one.

Mom,

To say that I was humbled would be an eternal understatement. When one of His servants pulled me aside at work and told me that I could send you a letter, I was "above the clouds" to make a heavenly pun about it. I asked the angel, "How much can I say?" You know how I love to negotiate. He said I could answer three of your questions. I took His offer to discuss with some of my closest friends and people I work with, as all of them have heard me talk about you for more than a decade. Although I can't explain the truth and completeness of paradise to you as I answer three questions, I feel grateful that I get to start you on some eternal thinking. I had seventeen years with you before I died and have been gone from you for fourteen years, so bear with me as I give this my best shot!

I asked the Holy Spirit to hold me while my friends and I picked three answers that would help you with your lingering pain, since you still exist within the limitations of the earth time-line. I get the privilege and experience of understanding both timelines, which clouds my choice about what to share with you. I know that three answers are about eighty-one fewer answers than you have questions, but I think this will help you heal. He gave me three, and He always shows that He provides enough to meet our needs.

Speaking of timeline, it has been fourteen years since He called me, and you were left with a void. I watched as everyone tried to comfort you after I was called to heaven. He held my soul during my funeral and revealed many marvelous things that helped me see why I belonged in eternity in 2007. He even revealed to me what He could not yet tell you, but He promised to tell you when you arrive up here with me. I was not blind that no one could comfort a mother who had just lost her one and only child of seventeen years. I was one of many people who wondered, "What is she going to do now?" We all know your life is an ongoing story with an unfinished ending; regardless, I still watch you and Dad in suspense, watching how you make decisions with a paradigm that doesn't have me with you. I see how you still respond when you are alone in the car and see a picture of another girl that reminds you of the old me. I see the lines on your face change when you see colors that remind you of me. Up here, there is no avoiding the truth. We all know that you will never really heal but only learn to live with the loss down there, but I do hold you up to the extent that He will let me.

Jeff Gaura

Mom, I am proud of how you keep in touch with my earthly friends. But unfortunately, there are a lot of other girls up here who also died early. Some of their parents found the act of staying in touch with the past to be too painful, and they retreated into a place where they ceased trying to make a positive impact in the world. Many tell me that they wished their parents had heard His teachings and followed them as you have.

For now, though, I have decided to use my three answers to comfort and hopefully enlighten you. I wish you could see the look of peace on my face as I write you this. Although I don't look the same, you will recognize me when you get here; that is one of His promises.

My first mystery to unwind addresses your ever-questioning mind. Sometimes, you still ask yourself, "Did I do enough?" To that, I want to offer you some peace. There is no way I would have been offered my job working at the foot of the throne of God without all that you poured into me. All those things that we both hated, late nights driving to events that neither of us loved, long meetings that end only with an agreement for another long meeting, etc., they taught me the patience I needed to explain life's mysteries to these little people. Those activities were worth every minute you and I invested in them. I use what I learned from those experiences every day. I know you thought my life was short, but everyone I care for is envious that I got seventeen more years than they did. So do not look back with any regret about what you were able to "finish" with me. I was perfectly finished doing this job. I had all I needed.

When I first arrived, I was greeted by a girl from medieval Europe who died at the same earth age. She was what we now call a sponsor. She took me to the Son and stood next to me as I stood in judgment. After I was received into paradise, she and I became great friends. Her mom also only had one daughter, and when her time on earth was up, she arrived in paradise thinking she wasn't ready to be here either. She petitioned the Father to be my sponsor, and she took me under her wing and tutored me. She led me around and introduced me to people, and I watched how they were spending eternity. Before the first moment was over, I was already starting to see that I was perfectly complete on earth and heaven. None of us on earth know when we will be called, but I was completely ready to come and serve in this continuum.

My second mystery ends with encouragement, and I had to get permission to share this one from one of the higher-ups. It does require more explanation than the first point. On earth, He teaches us with His word that we all have heavenly bank accounts, but while we are on earth, we don't get to see the ledger. Since I have left you in body, everyone here sees that you choose to spend a lot of what used to be mother/daughter time investing in other people. That banking stuff you taught me about systematic investing isn't just an earthly thing. Principle and interest accrue up here too. To say your balance is getting big is like calling Everest another large hill.

Mom, God is using the people who remain around you to change you to be more like Him. He went without His Son for a time; you are living without your daughter for a time. If you can put this letter down and stare at the ceiling for a moment, please do. Your response to this mystery is important to Him. His heart is for you to keep loving on people you meet, no matter what you know or don't know about them. What you are doing down there carries forward more than you can currently understand. Honesty in heaven is non-negotiable, and your efforts to befriend strangers make all of us up here who follow you see you as an example. I have watched how this burden He placed on you has refined you, and it is a beautiful outcome to watch from my eternity perspective. "Go, Mom, go!" is what my friends from the second century tell me when they see the spiritual equivalent of a replay from your life since I left you.

Everyone up here knows that a meaningful career is important to you. After all, so much of what you did for me was to ready me for my career. Therefore, I want to take all the remaining space in this letter to talk to you about what I do in my job. Although none of us have titles up here in a sense that I can convey to you, I can at least tell you what I do and whom I do it with and for.

Mom, I work with those who were not given a chance to be born. Do you remember how it says in His word that there will be "healing of nations" in heaven? All of us who work with them call them the "nation of the unborn." There are tens of millions of them, and it takes a lot of us to heal and care for them all.

All of those I serve spent one hundred percent of their earth time inside their mother's wombs, and they were the most confused when they arrived. They didn't have the same starting points the rest of us did. They had no regrettable relationships to disclose to the Father. None of them had words that they wished they had never used. None had any sin to say to Him when they stood in judgment other than original sin. Their judgment felt like a drive-thru experience on earth. They went before the judgment seat and left it so fast.

Upon arrival, most souls look for immediate answers (immediate is the best word I can come up with since time isn't linear up here) to the question, "What just happened?" These kids transition not from earthly light to heavenly light but literally from no light to most incredible light. My eternal career is that of mentor and caregiver to these children.

I get to answer their first question, "What is that?" when they see His light or when they see the trees full of fruit that they can pick and eat. I have held more than one of these little girls as they bypass the traditional first food of breast milk and take their first taste of eternal fruit. Mom, I am the one to feed some of them for the first time! I can't tell you the joy this brings to both of us. I get to hold them and look them in the eyes as their face lightens with the first use of their perfect taste buds. Their curiosities then evolve to question more than just the physical. I get to answer their imagination's calling when they hear His musicians for the first time, and they ask me, "What is that, and why does it make me feel so good?"

They have unique questions, more so than you ever thought mine was. For example, one of my first little girls asked me, "What does that mean?" when they heard their first guitar solo. Who thinks like that?

This also affords me a much broader range of access to heaven's resources. One time, a little girl asked me where the color blue comes from. I didn't know, and I asked the Holy Spirit to guide me with the answer. He answered me, and I said to the youngling, "I don't know, but let's go ask Him." Mom, I got to carry her up the stairs to the throne of the eternal and put her in His lap and watch Him minister to her! I brought her to Him and handed her to Him directly! I stood at arms' length and watched as He poured His Spirit into her and unwound the mysteries that were currently important to her. I had the best spot in the universe to see His infinite love and glory pour into this little person. He touched her and molded her petite body, making it perfect, and no being in the universe had a better view than me. We don't have words that get to the extreme nature of being in His presence. Some of my girlfriends who also work with the little ones have coined a phrase that we think works down in the earth timeline. We call it "infinite awesomeness."

There is even one thing better than what I just described. There are a few of us whom He allows to assist Him as one of the greatest mysteries of heaven is revealed, and I also get an up-close-and-personal view. The mothers of these little people sometimes arrive many of your earth years later than the children and are taken to the throne of judgment. Once the Son has presented them to the Father and He receives them into paradise, the Father always brings these women to Him and sits them in His lap and tells them, "Your pain is no more." Then, the heavenly rock concert starts! He doesn't give them any time (or me, for that matter), and He asks them, "Would you like to meet your child?" That is my prompt to bring the little one to the newly arrived mom and introduce the two of them. I hear their breath upon the first touch, and I watch the joy pass between the layers of eternity at this first union. Sure, there are many reunions up here, but reunions are minor compared to these first unions. It is another moment of infinite awesomeness that no one short of the Holy Spirit can articulate.

When the Father first told me that it was my responsibility to make first introductions, I asked Him how to do that. My soul was weak, and I could not fathom how He could select a girl who died at seventeen to administer this gift. I know we never developed foreign language skills in our household while I was on earth, but the Holy Spirit came and made me into a translator, but only between mother and daughter. That bond that exists up here is not the same down there, but the joy at the first meeting is nearly the same, I am told.

"Little one, you already learned those skills with your earthly family. I tell you, use your sense of humor. Use your servant's heart. Be prepared to answer endless questions. You know how to keep the focus off of you. Just do more of that. The Holy Spirit will come at your calling and refine you if your heart feels weak. I am here as well. Do not concern yourself with protocol or preparation. I picked you to do this job at the beginning of time and put you in place on earth to ready you for this moment."

That is partly a credit to you, Mom. Is that not the most fantastic story you have ever heard? Those weren't my words. Those were His words!

After doing the job for several of your years, I asked the Holy Spirit if I could participate in what you might call a "replay" of the first meeting between you and me. He paused before He answered me. I think He went to the Father before speaking. He said that I could watch it, but I had to wait until you got here so that we could watch it together. That should give you something else to look forward to. I sure am!

Those are my three mysteries for you. I hope they touched you and gave you some peace that your daughter is in a place where no superlative description works.

I know you always used to ask about my friends, so as a passing tale, let me tell you about them. He says that this doesn't count as one of my three answers. I work a lot with a girl from

Spain from the seventeenth-century timeline. She can go from tough as nails to loving and soft faster than anyone else I knew when I was down there. Another girl from second-century Egypt works with us, and she is so beautiful and strong. She has the same sense of humor I do, and even the angels joke with us when she and I are working the same shift together. She died early and worked as a volunteer at a synagogue when the Roman military took her earthly life. She is a true hero, as she is the only one of us who died proclaiming the Son. She has extra privileges that the rest of us don't. There is an aborigine from Australia in our group as well, and he is the most patient person in our group. I humbly admit that the kids probably love hanging out with him the most. He is the most affectionate of all of us, and he loves placing several younglings on his chest as he lays down, letting them explore each other in the safety of his protection. Living in the outback gave him a lot of time with the Holy Spirit, and he has a peace that none of us can understand, even though we are all in heaven together. One day I asked him where he learned to be so patient, and he said his joy came from investing a lot of time alone with Him every day when he was in your timeline. He figured out that being busy with earthly things has a negative eternal consequence. We are all a bit jealous that we didn't figure out the importance of unbusyness when we were down there.

For now, though, sleep well and stand tall! Your daughter is making a difference in eternity, and I thank you so much for what you did to nurture His eternal design for me. I love you across all places and timelines. See you soon, Mom.

Love,
Kristen

CHAPTER 3

A letter from Rover, the dog,
to his Little Master on earth

The wolf shall dwell with the lamb, and the leopard
shall lie down with the young goat, and the calf and
the lion together; and a little child shall lead them.
The cow and the bear shall graze; their young shall
lie down together; and the lion shall eat straw like
the ox. The nursing child shall play over the nest of
the cobra...

— Isaiah 11:6-9

"See, I make all things new."

— Revelation 21:5

Little Master, I am so happy now. The last time I saw you, we
were at the vet's, and I was an old dog. It hurt to get up and
down, so I was always lying down. You petted me a lot that day.

It was nice to have you lie down with me and rub me so much that last day. Then the vet gave me a pinch, and I went to sleep. When I woke up, I was up here with Big Master.

Big Master is the best master. Big Master says He loves Little Master. Big Master says you are coming up to see me one day. I am excited to see you again, and I have told the other dogs all about you!

Big Master is like Little Master. Big Master takes all the dogs to the gardens, and we get to run around and play all of our games again. We meet other dogs, and we get to meet all the other animals too. The cats aren't stupid anymore. The cats lie down with us now, and they are not annoying now. We are all young and fast, and the cats and dogs all talk the same language here. I understand all of them and don't have to bark at them anymore.

I met Marty. Marty is a dog's angel. Marty protected us when we were down there. We don't meet Marty until we are up here because we did not see Marty when he was down there. Marty showed us where he was hiding when we were down there. We did not see him, but he was there all the time. Big Master says Marty is like a dog. Marty is obedient and faithful, always waiting for his Master to come to him. I will take you to meet Marty when I see you.

Dogs pick their food now. There are no cans or bags or bowls or plates. We speak, and we eat what we speak for. Fruit is our favorite. We have many new dog friends. We are friends with horses and tigers, and some chickens and raccoons all want to be our friends. We all play together. There are many animals in our garden.

We were scared of snakes. Big Master told us a story about one snake. We were scared of him and barked a lot when we heard his story. The snake was like Marty, but he was stupid and didn't love Big Master. Big Master touched us after He told us the story of the snake, and we were not scared anymore.

Yes, it is nice up here. I will show you the garden and the rivers. We will go to the mountains and walk together. The other dogs up here do not bark stupid things that make us want to growl and attack them. There is beautiful music in the garden. It is better than the Little Master's exercise music from the garage.

Big Master said a dog's bark is more beautiful now, and Big Master says it is a blessing to all who hear it. But it is not like Rhonda said it was. I met your other dog Bingo. He was sad when he came up here. He missed you a lot when you divorced. Rhonda took Bingo with her. She was not pleasant to him, but he still loved Rhonda too. When you each were hurting, he did not understand why he had to hurt too.

Rover asked Big Master if it was his fault that Rhonda didn't love Lucky. Big Master loved him and played with him in the big garden. Big Master healed Lucky. Lucky is a friendly dog, and Big Master has fixed him.

I like Big Master's house. In Big Master's house, there are many doghouses. I have a bed here. It is comfortable. I am waiting for you to come and join me. Will you sleep with me? No other humans sleep up here. Will you try and sleep with me? I miss that. Maybe other humans will sleep with their dogs when you sleep with me.

I am friends with all of your dogs. We all wag our tails when we hear Big Master coming. Big Master showed us a picture of Little Master's life, and all the dogs saw how much you liked to walk into the woods, looking to shoot birds. All of Little Master's dogs enjoyed barking at birds for you. All the dogs liked carrying birds to you once you made them stop their awful noises.

I can't wait to show you all the roads. They are shiny like the foil you would wrap my bones in. There are no barking cars that hurt dogs. Other dogs walk with me on the shiny streets when Big Master has a parade. We like watching Big Master and the other Little Masters walk near us. They make dogs feel special. We feel how much you love us now that all the distractions from down there are gone.

Look, you are almost here. I am running to you. Big Master says that I should stand behind the Son. The Son is ready to hold your hand as Big Master tells Little Master all about Little Master. Dogs already know everything that Big Master is saying. We already knew it before we arrived up here. So all of your dogs now stand behind the Son, and we wag our tails.

Big Master says you are okay because the Son said you are okay. Once Big Master has told Little Master the big story, Little Master can stop hurting and play with all the dogs.

Jeff Gaura

You are here! Little Master is here! I see you, Little Master. Big Master is restoring you to the original Little Master. You look young again. You are beautiful like me.

Come, let's go to the garden right now. I want to introduce you to the new smells and see the new trails. You are at home now. This is Little Master *and* Big Master's home now.

And once the judgment was passed and the man was allowed entrance into eternity, he turned and saw that behind the Son stood all of his dogs, and all of them were wagging their tails. So he bent over and touched each of them, and they each spoke words to him for the first time.

And the man began to experience the healing hand of heaven promised to be part of eternity. And because of his dogs, he began to understand what his preacher on earth told him when he said that God will use everything to bring glory and that all things are made new.

And as his dogs began to lick him, the man started to feel the healing of nations, as the nation of dogs heals the nation of humanity on heaven, just as God intended for them to do on earth.

December 1, 2010.

God,

I suspect this will be my last letter to you. So let me
jump in with some gratitude; after all, I have a lot t
grateful for that I never saw when I was younger.

To start, thank You for all the people at the new chu
They come by and see me all the time. My cancer ha
gotten the best of me, and I can't speak to anyone no
but I see that they are there, and I hear them. My s
and grandson are there a lot, too. My two sons both
look alike, and I can't tell them apart anymore. Doug
never stays for long, and he doesn't read to me as Jeff
does. Thank You that two of my three children learne
the joy of reading. Thank You for Ms. Epstein; I
suspect she is with You already. Would You pass tha
message onto her?

Jerry has been wonderful to me, and he is the only one
that knows I can hear everyone. He reminds me all th
time about how we struggled wh

CHAPTER 4

A letter from an orphan girl to God,
written over the course of nine decades

Deloris Rita Barbier was born in Dunkirk, New York, on August 1, 1925. She was the only daughter of French immigrants, Edward and Barbara Barbier. Deloris' mother died suddenly in February of 1926, and Edward quickly remarried. Edward's new wife did not accept Deloris, and Edward elected to place Deloris into a Catholic orphanage in 1928. Edward had several additional children with his new wife, and Deloris interacted with her stepsiblings approximately three times each year when her stepmother allowed her to visit.

Deloris was the first orphan girl to graduate from the local high school. Once she graduated in June of 1943, she moved into the town's boarding house across the street. While riding a bicycle on a Saturday afternoon after the war was over, she was reunited with Jerry, a boy she barely knew in high school, and the two of them began dating. Jerry asked Deloris to marry him six months later, and the two of them started their life together.

Jerry took a job at General Electric and worked there for over a quarter of a century, transferring to the company's Syracuse location and away from his childhood family. During that time frame, they had two children: Dougie and Lucy. Twelve years after Lucy was born, they had a third child, Jeffrey.

After many years of working for someone else, Jerry took the great American risk. Jerry resigned at General Electric after earning the company's prestigious "man of the year" award and started his own business. He partnered with his brother Alfred, and the two of them began a tool and die company. Poor sales and a downturned economy caused the business to fail, and Jerry's life savings were depleted. After a bout of depression and a near-miss with suicide, Jerry chose to rebuild his life by relocating to warmer weather and better jobs. He moved the family to South Carolina, following his oldest son. With nothing more than a U-Haul truck of old furniture and kitchen items, Jerry, Deloris, and Jeffrey moved into a rental house and began their second iteration of living the American dream. At the end of their first year, they had set aside enough money for a down payment in a small but cozy home in a suburb of the capital city. Later, they left the Catholic church and joined their town's local Baptist church, a move even riskier for Jerry than starting a business. Nevertheless, they lived out their remaining years as active members of that church.

Deloris contracted breast cancer, and it metastasized into bone cancer. She died in January of 2011 at the age of eighty-six. She died in the presence of the three men who loved her the most: her husband, her youngest son, and her grandson. Jerry amazed everyone by living

Jeff Gaura

an additional seven years in their same small home, alone. He visited Deloris' grave nearly every day until he could no longer drive.

His family moved him to assisted living. As his health failed and the facility could no longer accommodate him, he was shuffled between temporarily living arrangements. Unlike his wife, Jerry died with dementia in 2019 in the presence of strangers at the ripe old age of ninety-four.

Their eldest son Doug died a year later, and nearly no one attended his funeral. His sister did not come, and his little brother intentionally arrived late.

These letters from Deloris to God happened once every decade or so, and they were her most passionate prayers as she struggled with God and His claims to love her and have great plans for her life.

OCTOBER 1, 1933

God,

Hello, today! The nuns say that we are supposed to talk to You every day. They teach us songs to sing to You each morning, and I love singing. They say we can ask You any question and tell You anything. They say talking to You is a good habit, so I will make it a point to talk to You all my life.

God, why did You take my mother? None of the girls at this home have mothers, but no one seems to know what we all did to deserve this. When I ask the nuns, they give me warm milk because I like warm milk. Why does asking about my mother have to mean a glass of warm milk? I am beginning to dislike warm milk now.

When I cry, the nuns don't hold me anymore. Instead, they clap until I stop crying and tell me that I must make my bed before eating breakfast and walking to school in the morning. Then, they say I am too old for that nonsense and I need to be a big girl.

I ask them when Daddy is coming to get me again. The nuns won't answer me, even though they know I love it when he comes. They say I can ask You, but You don't answer me either. You are a lot like the nuns.

When my father doesn't come to take me to his house, the nuns say You are my real Father. Do all fathers hide and not talk to and see their daughters? What do You sound like? When will I see You? I know the picture of You in the cafeteria, but how did the artist know what You looked like? I don't know what a mother is, but I think I know what a father does. He is invisible to everyone except artists.

Do You know why I like school? Ms. Epstein hugs me! Four kids share a desk, and three of them tell me about what it is like to have a mom. They tell me that their mom sits in bed with them and reads to them at night!

Ms. Epstein is teaching me to read, write letters, and work with numbers. She says my writing is beautiful. Do You know what else she does? She answers my questions. You should learn

Jeff Gaura

from Ms. Epstein that it is an excellent thing when you answer questions.

One more time. God, why did You take my mom?

AUGUST 24, 1941

God,

My junior year of high school starts in about a week, and I don't know what to do. A lot of the girls are going to drop out and get a job at the factory. The girls will earn $.30 per hour, with a promise of sixty hours a week of work. There is a lot I can do with $18 a week! The girls say they can move out of the home and no longer tell people that they are from the orphanage. I hate how people treat me when they hear that.

God, I want You to tell me what to do. I know You won't, and I need to treat these letters more like trips down a one-way street than a give and take of best friends. Yet, somehow writing to You seems to give me comfort. God, why is it that giving up the one thing I love the most is so tempting? Could You at least answer that?

On one side, the nuns tell me to stay and finish school, as it will be in my best interest. The best interest for what? They say that I have beautiful handwriting, and it would be a shame to see that talent go to waste. They said I should get my diploma and earn the right to be an executive secretary at the factory since secretaries make a dime an hour more than the girls on the shop floor. I don't know how to tell the nuns that the only reason I have nice handwriting is to please them. I want to tell them to shove it up the you-know-where!

I love learning, and I understand a lot at school; the other girls don't have the same feeling I do about school. A handful of kids make fun of all of us kids who are not from regular families. In junior high, the boys from the home would beat up anyone who talked trash to us. Now, those boys are going to war. From my perspective, those mean kids are why the girls are dropping out, not the promise of money at the factory. I must give up school in exchange for freedom from this place and $18 a week or stick it out and deal with the shame of being here. I could use some guidance here.

I don't know what to do about boys, either. All the ones from the orphanage join the military once they are old enough, and I don't know what to do about my desire to find a good one. The nuns say that even orphan girls can find a man who will love them some of the time, and then they can move out of this place, have children, and prove to the world that they are overcomers. They don't tell us how to do any of those things, though. I just keep hearing, "Get a man, get a man!" Then, after all of that non-sense, the nuns tell us not to have sex until we are married. The girls all tell me that sex is what the boys want, especially those who are home on leave from the military. I feel like I am doing a jigsaw puzzle, but they aren't giving us all the pieces or telling us what the picture on the outside of the box is.

To the boy's defense, I see many good things that happen when the boys join the military. They leave as boys come back looking like men! When they return and step off the bus, most of them go directly to the nuns to show off what they look like after basic training has made them bigger and stronger, and they show off their uniforms. All the nuns make us clap for them when they come back into the cafeteria. One boy was there, but he wasn't from the home. He came with a friend of his. He talked to me and told me that he liked the food in the home more than the stuff he got in basic training. We spoke for several minutes before he excused himself to go to town with the other boys. It was strange; I thought he would ask me to have sex with him, but he didn't. He was very respectful and never looked up and down my body like the other boys getting off the bus did. I think his name was Jerry. I will probably never see him again.

Sometimes, I sit with some of the girls and look out the second-story picture window on Saturday afternoon, waiting for the greyhound bus to stop. Those boys in green are so good-looking when they step off the bus and are in uniform! All the girls want to marry one of them, and they talk about which ones they want. I listen to them talk and pick out their men, but I don't have much to add to their conversation. Marrying one of those guys just seems above my lot in life, especially after all these girls are done with all their picking and choosing. The nuns are super serious when they say that good girls marry before they have children, so I don't see how I will have children. Sometimes, I just lay in bed and cry as I used to when I came home from visiting my dad.

God, if You let me have children, I promise to be the best mom to them and follow the rules. But I will need You to send me someone to teach me what to do. I don't want to treat my kids like the nuns treat us. That would be horrible.

I had some hope not long ago, but it didn't last. The nuns were teaching us in high school catechism that all hearts were evil. The mean boys looked embarrassed when she gave them examples of what an evil spirit looks like, and she started describing exactly what the mean boys do. They were ashamed, and they stared at the floor until she was done. I had some hope that they would see how horrible they behaved and would change. It didn't work. I hate it when You give us hope and take it away. If we are made in Your image, then I know where these boys get it from.

I have a technical question for You. When I asked the nuns why You don't honor my prayers, they say that prayers are more important to You if I say them during mass. They reiterate that where two or more are gathered together, You prioritize their prayers. Since I only go to mass once a week, maybe twice during Lent, I was wondering if there is some other place I can go where You will hear me. I talked to some of the other girls, and they agreed that they would come with me and pray as well, but we need to know where to go. One of the girls said that You were occupied listening to the prayers of the soldiers, and those were life and death prayers. I can see their point that bullies at a New

York high school aren't as important as what You need to give them to fight Nazis and Japs.

As a final request, and then I will shut up, would You please make the kids in Science stop saying, "Motherless, stupid, and it shows" when I don't know the answer? It isn't amusing.

JULY 5, 1944

God,

Happy July 4! I thought I would write You and let You know that I am delighted that I finished school. I am sorry for judging You. I can see that You used the nuns to answer my question. You are making progress in earning a bit of my trust. I have decided to trust that You will help the boys win the war as well. Perhaps if You let them win, I will become a nun!

The nuns surprised me and gave me the most excellent gift that I have ever seen them give any girls. They said I was the first girl ever to graduate high school, and they all clapped their hands and said they were proud of me. Then they gave me a suitcase, even though I don't need it yet. After all, everything that I own I can carry in a grocery bag. They said that a girl like me would go far, and they wanted to prepare me for my travels. That suitcase is the nicest gift I have ever received.

I moved into the boarding house across the street, and all the dropout girls are already living there. Two girls share a room, and we all ride the bus to the factory. We sing the way we did in

Ms. Epstein's class; it is perhaps the only time we aren't talking about the war.

It doesn't seem fair that the dropout girls work much harder than I do, and they often get hurt on the machinery. It seems unfair that I make more money than they do for easier and safer work. The factory makes the items that the men need to win this war. I am the executive assistant to the production manager, and I work with the purchase orders and vendors as part of the accounting department. This work is easy for me, and my boss, Mr. Miller, treats me nicely. Even though I am around people, I feel very lonely walking across the factory floor. The girls can't leave their machinery, even to go to the bathroom. I can go anytime I want. I am so glad I finished school.

Nearly all of the men of marrying age are away at war. I am beginning to wonder what Your will is, as I am about to turn nineteen next month and still have never kissed a boy. That leads me to another story that I wish You were there to help me. I visited my father's house yesterday. My stepbrother took me to the woods in their backyard and tried to have sex with me. There was no way I was going to let him do that, thanks to Sister Mary. On one of her days off, Sister Mary took me into the backyard and got real with me. She didn't wear her habit, and each had a glass of red wine and watched the sunset together. She told me that she was engaged before becoming a nun, but her fiancé was killed early in the war. She told me all about the birds and the bees, and she taught me what to do if a boy tried to take what wasn't his! I had no idea men were so weak when they get hit down there. If I hadn't seen my stepbrother act the way he did when I hit him with my knee, I wouldn't have believed it. On a side note, can You listen to Sister Mary's prayers? She still cries when she talks about her fiancé, Charlie. Never mind.

Taking the time to finish high school taught me that waiting for a reward isn't as hard as everyone makes it out to be. I am hungry to be married and have children, but I think I shall wait till the men come back from war. The dropout girls talk differently than they did when they were in the orphanage. They now say they will take any man who comes along, and some of them are dating the drunks and bullies who didn't have the courage to go off to the war. I have faith that this war will end, and I will get one of the good ones when they come home. If not, Sister Mary says that there is nothing wrong with a bottle of wine and nothing terrible about becoming a nun.

One of the things the girls at the boarding house have me do for them is read the newspaper aloud each night after dinner. They all learned to read, but none have done it since they started working in the factory. I teach them the meaning of the words; meanwhile, I read to them, and I love everything about teaching. Sometimes, I ask them, "What did I just read to you?" and let them feel comfortable answering honestly. If there is one lesson I learned in high school, it is to be kind to students and support them when they sincerely try. No matter what their answer, I always tell them, "A good try!" No one should ever have to hear, "That sounds like the answer an orphan would give."

Some of the girls have decided to take turns doing each other's hair on Sunday night, in case all the guy's come back. I am also saving up to buy a blue dress that I saw in Harry's department store window. The stepbrother yesterday said that blue looks good on me.

DECEMBER 25, 1948

God,

Merry Christmas! This is my first Christmas with Jerry, as we have been married only a few months. He tells me that it is our first house but not our last house. This place is a dive, but it is our dive. We have a kitchen table, but we only have one chair, so we take turns eating and serving each other. Jerry is everything that I dreamed of! And the part that comes with being a wife that the nuns don't get? Well, that is a real bonus!

Jerry saw me when I was riding a bike around town after he got back from the war. He ran over to ask me if I remembered him from his visit to the orphanage with his friend, and he asked me out on a date. We dated every weekend. Finally, he asked me to marry him, and of course, I said yes. Before we got married, though, we had sex. The nuns told me You don't listen to women who fornicate. That is why I waited until we got married to write

You this letter. Now that I am married and it is no longer fornication, I can write You again.

Most weekends, we visit Jerry's parents. Jerry's mother, Barbara, is my favorite person in the world. It was hard to believe that she almost became a nun. Her unconditional love for me has made me wonder, did You send her to me as a replacement for my mother? Granted, I don't know what a mother does, but I like how she talks to me and teaches me using stories, and she answers my questions. She always takes me into the kitchen and makes us a pot of tea. Then, we sit at her table, and she tells me of life back in Poland from when she was a little girl. Her stories of overcoming adversity are inspiring. She has a potbelly stove in her kitchen, and it is the most inviting room in the entire town of Dunkirk. I feel free to ask her all sorts of questions that I have never asked anyone before, even You! She tells me about how to treat a husband in a way that is different than the girls as they talk about their boyfriends. She always asks how Jerry and I are doing. She tells me all the time how proud she was of me for finishing school and getting out of the orphanage. Best of all, she calls me "darling," and she hugs and kisses me every time she sees me, even if it is in the grocery store. She makes me feel like a princess. She is sad that none of her other daughters-in-law come over and talk to her, and she prays about that hole in her heart. She deserves to be listened to.

Jerry and I are trying to have children. He wants seven, but I only want three. He was one of seven children, and that is too many. His company pays for me to visit the doctor, and the doctor says I can have as many as I want, but I can't tell Jerry that. I say to him that the doctor says we can have three with no problems. It isn't the whole truth, but it is enough of the truth.

I want to swear You an oath. If You give me children, I promise to be the best mother I can be. So please let me be a mentor like Barbara has been for me.

MARCH 3, 1954

God,

Where are You? Barbara died. I cried longer than Jerry did. There are so many times that she would answer my questions when You didn't. Right now, I need her more than ever!

You already know this, but I have a six-year-old and a two-year-old, and Jerry travels for work all the time. So I have to raise two kids alone. I sincerely regret my oath to You about mothering, and I will teach my children not to make promises to You.

We have some nice things because of Jerry's job, but I don't know what to do with these kids. I catch myself pretending that I am a nun when I talk to them. I promised never to act like a nun, yet here I am, doing exactly what I don't want to do! I know the nuns taught us that we would end up doing what we don't want to do, but I thought they were silly. How does this happen?

Since I don't have a car, I have to wait for Jerry to come home to go to the store, so I am at home by myself, figuring out motherhood as I go. Sure, this new house is lovely and much bigger, but getting to the store is so much harder in a subdivision. I still wish we lived in the city and could walk and get whatever I needed. Living in these big canned houses is the loneliest experience I have ever had.

The other housewives around here are as lost as me when it comes to parenting, and all of them had a mother. They like to smoke cigarettes and push the kids around in the strollers, and they gossip when we are at the playground. I don't want any part of that. So instead, I read out loud and sing to the kids and make up stories for them to ponder. Little Dougie seems to like stories a lot, but his imagination is too much for some of the housewives. He told Cindy's son Johnny that his dad died of a gunshot wound last week. Cindy and I watched him as he said it, and he seemed sincere and believable. Where did he get that idea? Cindy smiled at me, and I told her not to listen to kid chatter, but she took Johnny home when she heard that story. I heard her telling Johnny not to play with Dougie anymore.

When Jerry comes home from an out-of-town trip, it is awful in the house for the first day. He is overtired, as he doesn't know how to say no at work. He and all the other men who fought in the war now feel that they must fight as hard for General Electric as they did for the US Marines. I feel like a widow most of the time. I would say that we get one good day a week together as a family. He needs to get out of this job or find a way to say no to all these requests. However, that job pays for all the nice things that we have, and he doesn't mind working all the hours if he can provide for me. He thinks working at GE is like working to reach the beaches of Imo Jima. I don't understand either of those two things.

Dougie is out of control at home too. Even though she is only two years old, Lucy has already figured out that she needs to give him what she has to shut him up. If You love any of us, please protect her.

OCTOBER 10, 1965

It has been a long time since I have written You, but God, can You blame me? You have forsaken this household, haven't You? So I have decided to be courageous and tell You the truth, even if You don't respond to my tears.

Where do I begin? Well, Dougie comes home from school with Lucy. Then, I hear my little girl screaming, and I run to see what is happening. They both stop yelling when I walk in, but I find him tearing off her shirt and pants. I yell at him to stop and try to pull him off of her, but he just keeps going. It is disgusting to think about, let alone watch. Even at sixteen years old, Dougie has learned that he is the strongest person in the house when Jerry is out of town for work, and he has learned how to bully and physically intimidate both of us. I told him stories years ago about how scared and afraid all of us girls were when we were in high school of the bullies. I know he heard me! Now, he is one of the bullies. Where are You through all of this? Why haven't You protected Lucy? That was the very last thing I asked You to do!

I have stopped trying to get him off of Lucy. When I do, he retaliates. He holds me down with a knee on my neck while Lucy gets dressed. Lucy also yells at him to stop. When I tell him, "Wait till your father gets home," he pushes his knee on my neck even harder and makes me swear an oath to say no such thing, or I pass out. I am carrying another baby that should be due next month, and I am concerned about it. Please take care of this one even though You didn't take care of the last one.

I am too ashamed to talk to the housewives about Dougie, and they probably wouldn't believe it. They all love to watch him play baseball, as he is one of the best players on the team. He is a great pitcher, and he very much uses his bullying skills to help the team win. Sometimes, he throws a fastball directly at the head of the other team's best batter. When the hitter says something, Dougie looks him in the eye and slowly begins walking towards him. When he gets close, the umpire steps in between the two players and tells them both to stop. He walks back to the pitcher's mound, constantly turning around to make eye contact with the batter. Before he reaches the mound, he yells out, "You were warned!" More often than not, the kid gets scared and strikes out as Dougie's fastball is fast. All the dads at the games tell Jerry and me that we have a great son who will go a long way. They don't know the other Dougie and how he does that to his family. I am afraid he will go a long way to jail.

Most of all, I am scared for Lucy. She can't make him stop doing those awful things, and I am scared she will get pregnant. I am also too frightened to call the police, and You have decided not to get involved again. The bombing in Cambodia that is killing thousands a day is more important; I know I am supposed to understand that, but I don't.

I told the father at the church what Dougie was doing, and he told me to say more "Our Fathers" and "Hail Marys" when I thought about Dougie. But unfortunately, those prayers aren't working, just like these letters aren't working. So instead, I have Lucy sign up for more after-school activities to keep her safe. She is also riding home with the neighbor instead of taking the bus. She stays at their house and reads books until she hears her father's car pull into the driveway.

God, I think Jerry needs as much help as Dougie. When I tell him what happened, he beats Dougie so hard sometimes that I think his belt is about to break. Finally, Jerry tells Dougie that he is an embarrassment to the family. That makes Dougie stop for a few days.

AUGUST 25, 1968

God,

This is not shocking news to anyone up there with You, but You must be doing laundry or something and have let a preventable tragedy come to pass. I promised You that I would share with my children an appreciated love of schooling if You gave me children. Well, Dougie has dropped out of high school only two months before graduation. The teachers all told us that it was a mistake, and he had no good job to go to. I got one of the nuns to call him up after school and tell him my story, thinking he would listen. Unfortunately, he is not a good listener, even to stories about his mother.

The first thing he did when he dropped out was to get married. At first, his wife seemed like a nice girl, and I tried to treat her like Barbara treated me. However, she had a foul mouth, got angry, and raised her voice when she told me about how Dougie treats her. She thinks it was my fault that he was allowed to be so aggressive with women. I was hoping that she would at least like tea. She doesn't. She hates that he goes out and won't tell her where he is going or what he is doing. Jerry never did that, so I don't know what to say to her. Would You please put someone else in her life who can better help her? I don't have any of the answers that she needs.

Lucy is threatening to run away from home now, as she can't get along with Jerry. She has done well in school, but she hates how Dougie still preys upon her, despite Dougie being married. What am I supposed to do?

All that aside, I love the new baby. I promise not to let the same things happen to this one that happened to the others. I just need all these bad influences out of the house first. Would

You please let this one be okay and not end up like my other two kids?

SEPTEMBER 1, 1978

God, a lousy chapter with Jerry's family and that darn business has ended, and we have settled down here in South Carolina. It is hot in the summer, but it is worth it since there is no snow-plowing or winters spent inside. They all like tea here, but it is the wrong kind. They sit around and drink it cold, but they don't help each other with their problems like Barbara did. Instead, they gossip and never talk about what is really going on, and their favorite topic always seems to include the food. I still miss Barbara.

We have just moved into a lovely rental home, and Jeffrey is in school. Jerry still works incredibly long hours for his company, but we are out of the pain of losing everything. Jerry is working hard to see his dream of owning a home come true. He and I are trying to save up money for the down payment, and we are halfway there.

Jerry says he doesn't trust the economy. I think he doesn't trust You either, partly for the same reasons I don't. I am sure that many other people are praying for money, so I don't want to add to Your backlog of unanswered prayers, especially if it is the same thing that everyone else is praying for. The nuns used to tell me to pray for something new or important and not recycle someone else's prayer. I am over fifty years old now, and that is one lesson I have indeed learned. Money is one thing they said we should never pray for, but I don't think Jerry will be okay until he has enough to feel that we won't end up like his parents. His stories of being homeless in the winter of 1932 when he was seven years old still haunts him. He looks at the checkbook register every time the news says that one of these southern ice storms is coming.

AUGUST 31, 1988

God,

Thank You that Lucy followed in my footsteps and fell in love with learning. She is now a doctor and lives in Arkansas with her husband. She is a pediatrician; what a perfect choice for her! I don't know how to behave around her husband. He is a wealthy Jew, and I feel like he talks down to me. However, the two doctors I work for are nice Jewish men, and they treat me well, so I know it isn't every Jewish man that acts that way. For unrelated reasons, Lucy says that she is considering leaving him. Please, God, do not let that happen. She doesn't know what leaving her husband will do to her reputation.

Jerry got a call from his oldest brother, Ed. His brother Alfred died of a heart attack. Jerry said that it served him right after he lost all our money with that darn business. Please be there and listen to Jerry. After all these years, he is still mad at his brother's mismanagement of our money. He still thinks vengeance is possible even though Alfred is dead. I don't know how to talk to him about that.

Jerry and I have decided to teach Jeffrey to avoid girls at all costs. We are scared he might be like his brother since they have the same blood in them. Please don't let Jeffrey fall in love with the flesh of women as his brother did. Also, please don't let him have sex before marriage as I did. Having one child with a sexual disorder is more than enough for a lifetime.

DECEMBER 7, 1993

Lucy got divorced and remarried, and it is a Jewish guy again! But God, why can't You have her pick a guy who believes that You love us?

I like having grandchildren, but no one prepared me for how fast they grow up. My first granddaughter, Jenny, got pregnant and didn't tell me about it until she had an abortion. She said Lucy told her to terminate the pregnancy since she was not ready to care for it. Half of the girls in the home had babies before they turned eighteen. What is so different nowadays? How can Lucy recommend killing one child and spend all your working hours caring for others? It doesn't make sense. Where did I go wrong?

Dougie and our grandson Craig both got arrested and are now awaiting trial. We asked Jeffrey to move back home to help us. We are nearly retired, and we thought we had seen it all. Not a chance! We have to go to a trial and watch two generations of our children stand before the judgment seat of man. Jeffrey read out loud to us the transcript of their arrest inquiry. Dougie admitted to all the crimes. I knew this day would come when he was six years old.

Jerry made the last payment on the house, and he bought a bottle of scotch to celebrate. All of his brothers are dead now, and he feels vindicated. I suggested that we find a new group of people to make friends with, but he still resists being social in public. I wish he would let us both get out more. The people at the Catholic church all run out the door as soon as mass is over. We have been going there fifteen years, and I still don't know anybody.

My life would have been so much different if You loved me; that is for sure. Maybe Lucy's husband's ideas about You are right.

APRIL 30, 1999

God,

There have been a lot of significant events to celebrate since the last time I wrote You. Jeffrey got married, and Dougie and Craig are both out of jail! Katie and Dougie are finally divorced, once and for all, I hope. I am scared that they will try to get back together again. They did that once before, and their marriage was worse the second time than the first time.

God, Pat is the best thing that ever happened to Doug and perhaps the best thing that has happened to me since Barbara. She is perfect for me in this stage of my life. Pat met Dougie after he got out of jail, and she and I sit and drink tea. She doesn't have a lot of interest in gossip, thank God (that was a joke!). Interestingly, she talks to me a lot about the Bible. She has read it many times over. I think I am learning more from her than I have from all the years of going to mass. Perhaps I can get Pat to ask Jerry and me to go to her church instead of ours. She talks about the people there as if they are family. Please convince Jerry to give this other kind of church a try.

Jerry needs to retire soon. He has made all the money we need to retire. He needs to take care of stuff around the house more, including me. I want to have a garden, and I would love to have a lovely front porch that I can sit down at and drink the right kind of tea with my friends.

MAY 4, 2001

God, I have a secret. Everyone thinks that Linda's knee surgery has been challenging for the family. But this last month has been the best month of my entire life! Linda's mom and I are taking turns caring for our latest grandson Alex while Linda heals. He is only five months old, and I get to feed the baby and rock it to sleep every day that Betty isn't doing it. My daughter-in-law trusts my parenting skills, and she lets me do things my way.

Best of all, there are no housewives at the playground judging me anymore. If they are judging me, I don't care.

I use my suitcase every week to come to Charlotte to see the baby and help Linda. The nuns would be so proud of me now!

I have one small point to bring up. I am starting to get sick with breast cancer. It hurts, but I can live with it, especially with this baby to wake up for. If there is such as thing as a good time to get breast cancer, this is it! I can focus on others and not on myself. I know where this ends up, and it ends up with me next to You.

DECEMBER 1, 2010

God,

I suspect this will be my last letter to you. So let me jump in with some gratitude; after all, I have a lot to be grateful for that I never saw when I was younger.

To start, thank You for all the people at the new church. They come by and see me all the time. My cancer has gotten the best of me, and I can't speak to anyone now, but I see that they are there, and I hear them. My sons and grandson are there a lot, too. My two sons both look alike, and I can't tell them apart anymore. Dougie never stays for long, and he doesn't read to me as Jeffrey does. Thank You that two of my three children learned the joy of reading. Thank You for Ms. Epstein; I suspect she is with You already. Would You pass that message onto her?

Jerry has been wonderful to me, and he is the only one that knows I can hear everyone. He reminds me all the time about how we struggled when we first got married, and he holds my hand more than he ever has. He is by my side all the time, and he is talking to me every day about our life together, and he touches my hair, even though I can't move or respond to him. I hope he can see me smiling, but I can't tell anymore. Sometimes, he just starts laughing when he tells me a story. He is the only person here in hospice who laughs. I still need laughter in my life, even though I am dying. It remains my favorite medicine, well, that and the morphine.

When I hear Jerry talk to me, he sounds a lot like Barbara. I picture her when I see him speak. But, God, would it be possible to have Barbara next to me on judgment day? I am sure that I will be petrified, and there is no one on earth or in heaven who I want next to me when all my shortcomings are revealed. She is the only one who understood that starting as an orphan means that part of you ends life as one too.

Jerry is finally speaking to me of his regrets. He has cried to me and apologized countless times for all the times he prioritized work over family. He remembers how poorly he treated me after he came home from a business trip. He has apologized for not providing me with what was important, and he thinks Dougie's predatory behavior is his fault. Thank you for letting him see that it is okay to be honest with me, finally! He has enriched me like at no other time in our sixty-six years of marriage.

Jeff Gaura

This may sound crazy, but this has been our absolute best year together ever.

I want to tell him that nice things don't matter when your days are over, but he still wants to provide for me. Being homeless during the great depression wounded his soul, and I see he will never heal from all that loss.

When I am not here anymore, please take good care of him. He is woefully inadequate at taking care of a house, so please provide a cleaning service for him.

I remain very concerned about Dougie. He hasn't changed enough to be okay in the real world. Pat takes good care of him, but only to the point that he lets her. She is nearly a cripple, and Dougie travels a lot, just like his father did. I sure hope he doesn't do to Pat what he did to Katie when he goes out by himself. I heard he has a teenaged girlfriend on the side. Please protect that girl!

Thank You for honoring my prayers a long time ago for Jeffrey to be different. Thank you for honoring my prayers for Cinda to be safe and self-sufficient. She needed to be on her own to help her escape what her brother did to her.

Maybe I am delusional here, but I want to say thank You for this pain. I hate how it feels, but I love how it makes me think about eternity and You. Every relationship I have is different now. Very soon, I know that this will all be over, and I will be with You in paradise. I feel like the only thing that makes me make it between morphine doses is thinking about how You suffered on the cross for me. Breast cancer and bone cancer are bad. Even the oncologist tells me that bone cancer is the most painful one. Yet, I know this is nothing when compared to being betrayed by my friends and getting crucified. Pat has sure taught me a lot of things that I wish I had known earlier.

I think about what Pat has taught me each time I motion for a mouthful of Seven-Up. First, you only got a sponge filled with vinegar. Instead, I got a sweet beverage. Then, when I was in pain, I got morphine, and it started working as soon as they gave it to me. After that, all you could do was cry out, "My God, why have You forsaken me?" She has changed my view of You more than anyone who has ever lived.

God, I am so sorry that I concluded You ignored my prayers. You never stopped caring for me. I have had a great life.

Please take good care of this man next to me.

Please. I promise that will be my last prayer ever.

GOD'S RESPONSE TO THE ORPHAN GIRL AFTER HER ARRIVAL IN PARADISE

"Dearest Deloris, it filled my heart greatly that you were able to acknowledge at your mortal life's end the many blessings I poured upon you. Your angel and I intended for you to learn it much earlier. Your angel was loyal to you, but he also was alone every time he presented My presence to you only to see you miss it. He asked Me to tell you that he misses you, and he loved how sincere you were when you struggled with Me. He called you his 'Little Jacob.'"

Doris stood as the Father continued. The Holy Spirit held her upright as God's truth humbled her core identity.

"Now that you are here, I will answer your questions as I have promised, and I will help you begin your healing journey. Above all things, this moment of reveal is special to Me more so than it ever will be to you, as the events of your life not only grieved you, but many of them grieved Me."

"I thought You controlled all things, don't You?" Deloris said.

"Only to the extent that you let Me. I have also given the enemy some authority on earth, and seldom do people take the time to look for the differences," He said.

"To begin, your mother was never meant to die early. Your father was abused as a boy, and he, in turn, abused her. The details of those events will heal no one present; that is a conversation between only him and Me." God turned His head and smiled, allowing Deloris a chance to trust Him in a way that she never did on earth.

"I will tell you that your father felt remorse and shame at his role in her death. He suffered at least as much as you did, as she was the greatest gift I ever gave him. He failed to cherish his first wife. He felt like he had no choice but to push you away as an act of contrition for his second wife. Your stepmother never loved you, as she was jealous of your father's love for you. I know you think you were the only one who cried when you left their home, so let Me reveal what happened."

And with that, Yahweh allowed Deloris to watch a replay of the events of her father and stepmother's marriage. She repeatedly watched as her father pleaded with her stepmother to allow Deloris to live with them. She watched the rage in her stepmother's eyes as she tore out hair from her head as she insisted that Edward prioritize the children they had together, no matter the cost. She observed the request that her stepmother presented to her father and the depression and isolation he felt. He had already lost one wife due to poor choices; he was not prepared to lose another. She also watched her stepbrothers and stepsisters as they responded to their parents' fights. She watched as an evil spirit entered into her stepbrother that convinced him to attempt an intimate act with her. Finally, she watched a replay as her angel combatted the evil spirit in her stepbrother, and she saw how Yahweh transcended time and place to use Sister Mary's teachings to keep her safe.

Deloris shook her head and began to weep as the healing started. However, God stepped up and wiped the tears from her eyes.

"I also keep My promises to wipe the tears from your eyes, as these are tears of healing that cannot be unmade. So come to Me until your soul is settled, then I will continue."

"I had no idea how much all of them hurt inside!" said Deloris as she stepped into God's arms.

Jeff Gaura

"Yes, the sins of the father pass-through for many generations, I have said," repeated God.

Deloris's mind raced forward to Dougie, and God saw her anxiety build. His healing hands began touching a deeper layer of the required mending. He caressed her head and repeatedly kissed her, allowing the Holy Spirit to pour into her and anoint her with a peace that the world cannot understand. She could feel that He was about to open eternity to her, but her wounds were deep and needed care. So instead, He spoke to her of the mystery of generational momentum.

"I intended for you to demonstrate an academic focus, and I gave you tests to encourage you to see how I gifted you. Many others with similar talents cast them aside and did nothing to nurture them, much like the man with one talent in my parables. You finished school despite the repeated efforts of the enemy to convince you to stop. In that act, you started and became proficient in the use of your mind. Let me show you how I gifted you, and you passed this forward to your offspring."

With a single motion of His hand, Yahweh presented Deloris a replay as each of her three children pursued academic endeavors. She watched how each responded when they were given complex tasks, and she watched all of them exceed with an air of confidence as they approached the unknown.

First, she watched Dougie make great architectural drawings, then use his hands to make the pictures come to life. He built homes, cars, and structures from images in his mind, and they were the envy of many.

"He learned to organize from you," God said.

Next, she saw a scene of Lucy studying vast amounts of medical knowledge, sorting out what was essential and what could be looked up later when it was needed. Her focus was extraordinary in times of crisis, and she could separate critical and unimportant with no knowledge of any subject. Then, she would use it to save people's lives.

"She followed your lead," God said.

Lastly, she watched Jeffrey put together many talents into one being. He ran many businesses and was a powerful public speaker. He mentored younger people, and he poured his time and his money into those around, never owning a nice car or fancy clothes. She watched as he remembered Deloris' teachings about working too much, and he retired long before his father ever did. And in all his works, Jeffrey talked about God.

"Jeffrey learned by listening to you lament to Me. He was listening when you thought I wasn't," He said.

After a few moments of watching history replayed, God spoke again.

"Now, watch what they did when you were not looking, little one."

Again, He motioned with His outstretched hands, and she watched her children do work assigned to them when no one was watching. They all completed complicated mathematics quicker than even their angels, and she saw each of them reading out loud, inspiring those around them.

"They all learned the power of reading from you. None of their teachers in school could do it as well as you," He said.

Deloris got a special moment when she watched Lucy read her mother's medical journals when she was only in middle school. Deloris had left them on the dining room table one afternoon, and Lucy would read them cover to cover when no one was home, trying to learn what it was that made her mother so bright. Lucy yearned to be a part of medical procedures performed in their offices. Lucy would get hungry and thirsty but would not get up until she finished all the journals Deloris brought home.

"Now, watch this, little one," said Yahweh as He moved His hand and a multidimensional screen appeared, and she watched her daughter twenty years later. Deloris viewed a supernatural replay as Lucy prepared for her medical school graduation. The paper document she was to receive was a proclamation that she had earned the title of doctor of medicine. She watched the pride and joy on Lucy's face as she put on her blue graduation gown, hat, and the unique tassels that only someone earning an MD can wear. She looked at herself in the mirror and smiled with no one watching her. She spun herself around in a circle to watch her robe whirl in the wind; then, she stopped her playing to allow a few tears of joy to fall down her perfectly powdered cheeks. She whispered under her breath, "Thanks, Mom," as she wiped them away.

Yahweh pulled Deloris into His chest and allowed His light to fill her with the purest love she ever felt.

"Very well done, little one," He said.

"Allow me to show you a piece of the future. Just like a mustard seed grows into a large, beautiful plant, look what has become of your little Lucy." Yahweh again allowed Deloris to watch on His big screen as Lucy practiced her skills as a neonatologist and helped hundreds of preterm babies survive horrendous birth situations. She watched the confidence Lucy put on display with the nurses and the administrators as she would petition to try new procedures when none existed, trying to save the lives of children who might not get a second chance at life.

"Part of you lives in her, little one, even now," God said. Deloris's breathing became shallow as she embraced the impact of her efforts.

However, God was not done with His showing off. "Come, see what has become of your youngest!"

Deloris sat up and observed something she had never seen. God's replay showed her seated at the kitchen table, reconciling the family checkbook each month. Even though he was only ten years old, Jeffrey watched her account for every penny each month. God then moved to the future, and she then watched as he got back his final examination in advanced differential equations as a junior in college. He received the only perfect score

Jeff Gaura

in a class of over three hundred students. Just like his sister, she watched him whisper, "Thanks, Mom," under his breath. Finally, she watched Jeffrey reach up and put a copy of his diploma showing his earning his degree from an Ivy League university, making the distinction of *summa cum laude*. There, at the front of the scrapbook, was a faded picture of Deloris and Jeffrey.

"Your youngest is now My full-time servant, and he writes tales to touch the hearts of those who don't understand Me. He could never have done that without you. He avoided the love of money that Jerry could not do. He chose not to be a fool and work beyond the appointed time. Your children were only able to do these things because of what you demonstrated. This one now leads by example and perseverance. You provided him confidence in times of difficulty that few do. So many parents talk about their work; you did the work in front of them."

"Thank You," she said.

"Next, you had many questions about your mother-in-law, and I will answer you now. I did place Barbara in your life to replace your losses. I placed her there at your time of greatest need. But she was not meant to teach you about mothering. She was meant to teach you how to be a wife to a man with many insecurities and scars from being homeless and fighting in a world war. I know you thought that being a mother was the more important, but your role as his wife lasted you until your final breath; remember, Jerry was the only one who held your hand until the end. Your role as a mother was gone many years before your role as his wife came to an end. It was your need to be a wife that was greatest, not your role as a mother. So many women get this wrong to this day. I did not want to see that happen to you."

Deloris stared straight ahead.

"Barbara would not have been able to help me with Dougie, would she?" she rhetorically asked.

God hugged her and wiped more tears from her eyes, just as He promised He would.

"No, she would not have been able to help you. Indeed, it would have hurt her to be a part of that story just as much as it hurt you. When I called her to be with me, I was also protecting her from Dougie." He said. He gave her a moment to ponder the impact those words made before He continued.

"You often prayed for your children to avoid trouble. What you call trouble is also what my writers speak of as the Refiner's Fire." Deloris paused and spoke out loud.

"Pat talked to me about the Refiner's Fire."

"I wanted them to learn from their troubles above all else. You never could allow yourself to see the truth that they were the ones who made these bad choices. Instead, you held yourself accountable for behaviors that were not your responsibility. They picked poor marriage partners, and they chose both illegal and immoral actions. It required your government to imprison your oldest son and your grandson before they would hear My message. Your daughter Lucy was irreparably hurt, and she never would submit to My care with complete abandon, even when

Jeff Gaura

she knew in her heart that this was the best choice. Your prayers were heard, but there were other aspects of free will in place that prevent their fruition."

He waved His hand again, and before her were repeated scenes where His servants presented the message of Christ to Lucy, only to see her reject it. Deloris was about to speak, but God intercepted her thoughts and spoke first.

"Of course, I am not done with Lucy. Even though she pushes people away, My servants come to her and share the message of hope My Son offers to the world. My hope remains strong that she will take My free gift very soon."

"So do I, Father!" she said.

"Yes, your daughter and granddaughters deceived you by not telling you about their predicament when they were pregnant out of wedlock. Each of them will get to meet their daughters that were intended to be their children once they arrive in heaven, and it will be the first union for both mother and daughter. I have decided to give you the best seats in the house when your daughter meets her son for the first time. You will also get to meet your grandson for the first time at that moment. You will sit on My lap, and you will see My divine will pass before you, and you will be amazed at what you did not understand when you were on earth."

At that moment, Deloris and the Father were transported to the Lamb's judgment seat, and she watched God take His seat.

"Only you will be seated near Me when your granddaughter meets her son for the first time."

"She was also meant to have a son?" she asked, covering her mouth in joy.

"Yes, little one. I made them, male and female. I made them."

In the next moment, He transported Deloris to the heavenly library. Deloris was surrounded by books that glowed, and God sensed that she could not wait to open them and begin reading them.

"This will be the last place I visit with you today. In due time, you can open and read all these books. I have decided that I will allow you to teach the contents of these books to newcomers in the same way that you taught the dropout girls seventy earth years ago. This is part of your crown in heaven that I promised you for your good works on earth. Turn and behold your impact."

Deloris turned around, and several of her childhood nuns were behind her, as were many of the dropout girls. Sister Mary was in the back, and she stepped forward. They all stepped forward and embraced her. Once they were all done, they all clapped and looked at her. Sister Mary spoke up.

"Welcome, Deloris. You are the most successful investment of time and love I made when I was on Earth. It is an honor to see you standing alone with our Father here in eternity. You deserve all that He is pouring into you," said Sister Mary.

Deloris reached out and took Sister Mary's hands and looked her in the eye.

"Sister Mary?" she said.

"You can just call me Mary. Everyone here is a brother or sister," she said, making everyone laugh.

"Did you get to see Charlie once you arrived?" she asked.

Mary broke eye contact and began laughing loudly.

"Yes, I did!" she said. They both laughed and hugged one more time.

"He and I see each other every day! I will introduce you to him," she said.

"Come, Deloris, I have one more place to take you," said the Father. He led her down a hallway away from everyone else in the library. This was a private section of His mansion.

"You only began to see how I did not forsake you when you were nearing the end of your days. Seldom did you see Me next to you. You read to the girls who were scared to read out loud, and you encouraged them. That was My Holy Spirit working through you. You reached out to Katie like Barbara reached out to you, and you took a great risk to do so. Katie was burdened by an evil spirit that you could not understand. Still, your words prevented that spirit from traveling to the next generation, and your prayers against it bound it in Katie and kept it from occupying her children or her children's children. In the same way Lucy was raped, so was Katie."

"Really?" Deloris was in disbelief, but she knew that God could not lie. He let her pause to embrace this moment of eternal learning. Finally, God pulled her into His chest and hugged her yet again. He bent down to look her in the eyes.

"I am proud that you saw the pain of your breast cancer refined you. Cancer was not intended for you, as cancer is not from Me. However, I could use it to let you see how close I have been to you all of these years. You could have easily become bitter and caught up in disagreements with your health care professionals to delay your inevitable ending. Instead, you chose to show Me sincere gratitude that you could see the connection between longsuffering and what it means to abide in Me."

"Really?" she said.

"Without your graceful submission to the path that breast cancer places on a woman, your husband would never have been real with you. While you were departing the old world, your grace allowed him to heal from his guilt and perceived failure to take care of you and your children. The peace that you wore on your face while struggling with breast cancer saved your husband, Deloris."

"Really?" She could think of no other word to use.

"Many yearn for these next words, but it is in your life, presented before Me, that they come to pass."

With that act, God lifted her into the air by raising His hands before words poured from His mouth as water flows from a fountain.

"Well done, My good and faithful servant. Come and receive your Father's love. It is what you have always wanted."

And with that, Deloris felt the Father's depth and warmth as His healing touch refined her and lifted scales from her soul. She was now finding the rest and peace that He promised. Her soul became lighter as remnants of her damaged life on earth were stripped away, a new hope emerged, and God sensed it coming. He was expecting it.

"God?" she said.

"I know what you are about to say," He said.

"So, what is your answer, then?"

"Turn around. They have desired this as much as you do."

Deloris burst with joy as she knew what was about to happen. The core of her being had yearned for this moment since she was a little girl. This time, she knew that this Father would honor His promises and remain with her forever. She smiled as she felt a trust unlike any she ever experienced on earth. Then, as she turned and saw the deepest desires of her heart filled, she screamed in joy.

"Mom!" she yelled out.

Next to her was Barbara.

"Honey, Barbara and I have been talking about you for forty years. Welcome home."

And for the first time, she heard words from her mother's mouth, and it sounded a beautiful note in her soul. After a moment of hugs, Barbara spoke first.

"Come, would you like to have a cup of tea? I hear that you still like it. We have set the table for four!"

Deloris spun around to look for the Father, and He remained where He was.

"Who is the fourth seat for?" she asked.

"You know…," said God.

"It is for Pat, isn't it?"

"Of course, it is. Barbara is looking forward to teaching her my tea recipe too."

"Indeed," He said, as He left them to drink tea in His library and catch up with each other. For all of them, it was a great reunion.

CHAPTER 5

A letter between
Confederate Lieutenant Donald White
to his commanding officer
at the Battle of Gettysburg

What is causing the quarrels and fights among you?
Don't they come from the evil desires at war within
you? You want what you don't have, so you scheme
and kill to get it. You are jealous of what others
have, but you can't get it, so you fight and wage war
to take it away from them. Yet you don't have what
you want because you don't ask God for it. And even
when you ask, you don't get it because your motives
are all wrong—you want only what will give you
pleasure.

—James 4:1-3

General Heth,

If I can't report from the battle line, I will declare to you from the line into heaven. I know you planned to try to make it to Harrisburg or even see our brigade standing strong in Philadelphia, but the last thing I remember was getting hit by slug when my jenny[1] got jacked. That rifle should have killed that highfalutin union boy running at me, but all I got was a flash in the pan[2]. I tried to stand up and move, but all I heard was ringing in my darn ears as I lost blood from the right side of my chest.

"Lieutenant, let me get the meat wagon!"[3] my sergeant yelled at me. I waved him off. I told the company to cross over McPherson Ridge and leave me to be, and that is what they did. I am proud of the horse sense[4] of my Virginia boys for following orders. You always told us that obedience is the secret to godliness, both in victory and in defeat. My men did right that day.

Yet here I am, a dead man, looking at eternity and my judgment knowing it is now my time to acknowledge the corn[5]. When I turned to look at the size of this line I am in, I shouldn't have been shocked, but I am. I can't count that high, but a boy from Kentucky in front of me says it is over forty thousand. When I asked how he knew, he said the Holy Spirit told him. You never taught us nothing about God and His minions doing counting for us, so I just called His numbers a bunch of balderdash.

When I first arrived and was told where to wait my place, it was discouraging to see all the people. I told myself to think of it like trying to get into the mess hall down near the Tidewater

Jeff Gaura

during training camp. As we waited, I figured the best I could and decided the Kentucky boy might be right, and I would have wagered at a bottle of moonshine that forty thousand was about right. These soldiers start showing up in the line in waves like June bugs do. Sir, there were a few pogs[6] in line, but most of the fine folks in line were us, soldiers. You know, there were some good old folks from the country, and a couple of pale skins from Europe were mixed in there. There were some of them chinky-eyed folks from the Orient too. There was even a couple of them stupid blacks. It made me wonder how that could have happened.

While I waited my turn at the judgment seat, the jeep[7] standing next to me and I would take turns checking in with our brothers to see what was going on. The jeep would hold my spot in line when I would go to the back and hear from the other joes[8] what the latest story from Gettysburg was. I would ask them questions kind of the same way you would ask me when I came back from the lines in Fredericksburg, "Who did you see? What did the battle line look like? Which set of troops seemed to be moving the most? Where were the cannons?" Stuff like that.

The first two boys I talked to were from General Iverson's brigade. They were south of Oak Hill when each took a slug in the chest. They were running out in the open, and they should have known better. They went on to tell me that nearly everyone on both sides was engaged in the battle the day after I died and that I missed most of the bloodshed. I can't say that any man misses bloodshed, but I took him at his word and figured I must have died early in the fight. We are all guessing that it didn't take very long to get the heathens to surrender, but the size of the darn line made us keep wondering what was going on and why it was still getting bigger.

A mighty peculiar thing happened next, and I feel like you need to know this. After talking to the boys from Oak Hill ways, I walked back another few hundred steps and spoke to some boys who were laughing and looking proud. I suspected that they had some good news for us. Instead, they shook up my whole view of this thing.

"Where were you boys at?" I asked.

The tallest of them spoke first. He had a funny accent. Said he was from Rhode Island. I suspect he saw on my face that the real question I was looking to get answered wasn't that.

"You mean, how is the battle going? We can't say. We just got to the top of Culp Hill when General Greene told us to wait. Everyone else was leaving to help Longstreet, and our brigade was the only one not packed full of jeeps. Next thing you know, all of us hear the inbound cannons and now look. We are up here with you southern yokels."

Greene was a part of the Union oppressors. There was no way that they would be in line to get into heaven, could they?

"How are you boys here? I mean, how did…" I started to say, but the older guy in their lot with the white beard interrupted me.

"You mean how did we get up here and not end up in hell? Is that what you want to ask?" he said. He was angry and speaking fast, just like them darn yanks tend to do.

"Uh, yeah," was what I said. He pointed his finger at me, looked me in the eye, and continued with his rapid-fire chatter.

"You know, you are not the first fool to think we aren't supposed to be in this line. And none of my boys aren't strange to be thinking the same thing of yins."

That fired me up, sir. I jumped into the fight and let him have it.

"You think we had some sort of choice in this mess? You and all your northern aggression tactics were trying to take what was rightfully ours from us, and I am not just talking about the stupid blacks. You were trying to tell us what to do and not do and where we could be selling all our cotton and tobacco. Then you got this idea to tax us, even after selling all of it to y'all! It is like you fools have completely forgotten that taxes are the reason our grandparents fought to start this country in the first place. All of your shenanigans are nothing short of organized crime. So yes, I am wondering who made a mistake and how in the hell did you get in this line?" I was fit to be tied.

He didn't hesitate to throw one or two shots back at me.

"Attacking Fort Sumter without warning and killing people just because you can? Is that what your mother taught you to do when you disagree? Just get out a gun and kill folks who had nothing to do with your disagreement? It sounds like your Bible is missing all the pages in Exodus where it says, 'thou shalt not kill,' from what I gather. Either that or you think the Good Book is a bunch of suggestions that you can take or leave like a page from the newspaper that yins don't know how to read."

His fellas patted him on the back, telling him that he did well to tell me off like that, but he kept coming before I could get my first word out.

"You boys can't read. That is your problem, right there. Instead, you numskulls go right to the guns to solve your disputes. You were stepping onto someone else's property and shooting at the folks who did nothing to you. Is that how your momma taught you to make things right? You can call our taxes organized crime. You boys are all the real sinners. Now, look at all of us, you and me! We are both in this line, and neither of us thought we were supposed to get here this quickly," he said.

I didn't know what to say to all of that, as none of the boys around me were stepping up to defend me. I left all that humbug and went back to my spot near the front of the line. I told the jimmy to go for a walk and take a stint at talking to the sleeves[9] behind us. I promised I would hold his place in line for him while he was gone.

When the jimmy came back, I figured out he wasn't just another fresh fish. He pointed out a couple of oddities that I missed. First off, no one needed to hit the head[10] while we waited in line. Usually, long lines like these make a man need to go like a racehorse. Secondly, no one wanted to hit the racks[11] either.

I suspect you taught us something about this, but I expected to spend time in heaven doing some sleeping. Boredom doesn't make a man sleepy in this particular line, either.

I will check back in with you once I get closer and can see better.

FRONT OF THE LINE IN SIGHT

Sir, I am near the front of the line now, and I have watched a couple of intakes from afar. Until I got up here, I thought this whole situation was fugazi[12]. I mean, the war was messed up, and the chatter at the back of the line was just as messed up. However, I took a liking to a chaplain in the queue who was a long way behind me. He told us that everything would be changed once we get to the front of the line because we were in between earth and heaven in a space called purgatory, and everyone awaiting trial has to spend some time here since Jesus' second coming hasn't happened yet. Why didn't you ever mention this, Sir?

I never called it a trial before now. I always thought of it as a judgment that had already happened on earth when we believed in Jesus Christ as the Son of God. I thought we were good to go, and as soon as we died, meaning we went right into heaven, no stopping in the middle for food and water. That chaplain got my attention, though. He quoted some Bible verses he had memorized, kind of like the way you had some verses memorized, but not meaning any disrespect, sir. He had a lot more of them than you did.

> Then I saw a great white throne and him who was seated on it. From his presence, earth and sky fled away, and no place was found for them. And I saw the dead, great and small, standing before the throne, and books were opened. Then another book was opened, which is the book of life. And all the dead were judged by what was written in the books, according to what they had done.
>
> — Revelation 20:11-12

When he finished, he put his hands on his hips like he was a grandma walking in on me doing something I wasn't supposed to. We all felt a bit of shame.

"You boys dead or not?" he asked. We were a mixed group of boys from both the north and the south.

"Yes, sir, we are." Both sides of the boys said the same thing.

"And are you going to be judged according to what you have done or what someone else has done?" he said, making eye contact with a different lot of us.

"What we have done, sir," was all any of us could say.

"Well, you boys are going to reach the front of that line and see what is going on, and it won't be about your uniforms or your rank or any of that. Those are the things of the old world.

We are about to either be given entry into heaven or denied it. I myself am looking forward to seeing His face. How about you?" he asked.

A few boys nodded, but most of us looked at the ground. The chaplain had a lot more confidence than the rest of us. We all looked like hospital rats[13] more than we did like soldiers when we all realized that we were unsure what was about to happen. After all, all of us died trying to kill the other man, and that just wasn't a good look for either side.

Truth be told, that chaplain's words hit us like a bunch of bricks falling on us. All of us, both from the north and the south, looked at each other differently from then on. The tall guy and I talked about how we killed our brothers and were ready to do it again in our hearts. For my part, I apologized to him, and he did the same to me, and we shook hands.

Then we started some real talking, and the chaplain stuck around and watched, but he didn't say anything. We figured out that each coveted what the other side had. We sure wanted their factories and transportation systems. They sure wanted all of our cheap resources and stuff we grew with our negros. Then, we both figured out that we were fighting each other and trying to kill each other on the Sabbath, and we were not following God's instruction about having a day of rest.

Another boy from that Rhode Island lot and I talked, and we figured out that we had made our flags into idols that we used to justify our killing sprees. General, that is half of the ten commandments right there that we have been doing wrong, and that is just in the last two days. Both north and south thought that if the chaplain was right, this might be a real short trial because we were all guilty. I am telling you the truth; it was a mess when we figured out that all of us were Christians and still committing the worst of sins against each other.

We got near the front of the line and rounded the final corner. We could now finally see what was going on. Let me tell you. I could spend the rest of the day just talking about all the busyness at the throne of God, but that would take more words than I know how to use. But I will tell you a few things.

The first thing that caught my eye was about two dozen folks wearing all-white bed linens, and they each had a fancy crown on their head. They all surrounded the throne and parted as each of us went before Him for judgment. I started looking at each one of them a bit closer. General, I do not know how to tell you this other than to say it outright. Some black-skinned folk was in that lot of the white sheets, and they were next to the throne. I know you said that this wasn't possible, but I saw it with my own two eyes, sir. There were some stupid blacks in that two dozen. And if that is not enough to rattle you, there were some chinky-eyed folks in there, too. Again, sir, I saw it myself. It was natural, no matter how unreal you might think. I'm sorry, sir, but those are the facts, and you always told me to give you the facts, no matter how much they hurt.

I need to talk about the floor around the throne that everyone was standing on, as it caught my attention. That floor looked like a blend of glass and fire, if that makes any sense, and some of the white sheet folks were playing instruments of the likes I have never seen before. They looked as happy as we did after Fredericksburg, all smiling like they had defeated some sort of enemy. One instrument looked like a fiddle, but it had a lot more strings, and the ringing that came from it sounded like a whole darn band was playing. A couple of folks were with the same sort of heavenly fiddle, and they were playing harmony with the first fella. A dark-skinned man was playing an instrument that looked like a harp, but it sounded like a nice bugle. How is that possible? One of the chinky eyes people was playing a melody on a guitar with new strings on it, you know, all nice and crisp sounding. Sir, it sounded like a marching drum-like Corporal Thomas played when you would have him walk up-front.

A couple of us watched with our mouths opened as the musicians, if that is even what they were, started changing colors. I don't mean the people changed colors. The clothes changed color, and those sheets would go from white to purple as fast as you could snap your fingers. When they would stop playing, they would switch back to white. The boy two in front of me was from West Virginia, and he thought the skin color might be changing as well, but I looked. The black folk remained black folk. Just like you said, sir, blacks will always be stupid blacks. Apparently, that is true in heaven, as well.

I am saving the best story for last. God is truly on His throne, just like you said He would be. It was getting close to my turn, and I could now hear what was happening with the guy in front of me. When God spoke, it was like a thunderstorm would happen right over His head. Then, the enlisted folks around the throne called me. It was now my turn.

THE JUDGMENT

"The time for judging has come," He said, and the next thing that happened, well, where do I start?

I fell to my knees. Then, I could now understand the words of the song they were singing. They were saying, "Marvelous are Your works, O Lord God, the Almighty. Just and true are Your ways, O King of the nations. Who will not fear You, Lord, and glorify Your name? For You alone are holy. All nations will come and worship before You, for Your righteous deeds have been revealed."

I had heard that verse before, and I knew what it meant. It came from the end of the Book. From my new vantage point, I could see the seven lamps that were next to the throne. They were all lit up, and what flowed from them seemed to be the same sort of power and spirit that flowed from Him. I can't describe it, General. I suspect you will just have to wait till you get here to see what I am talking about.

He moved His arm one time, and it seemed as if time stood still. It was as if I were no longer in front of the throne but was now in some other place, and the only thing I could see was all of my deeds. There were many good deeds, and without question, the enlisted folks and the white sheeters who worked around the throne praised me for being so willing to lay down my life for my brothers in arms. They also talked about how well I took care of my mother when she was dying, carrying in the firewood for her all winter and making sure she got some meat every week to keep her blood strong. God also put on the screen how I would step in and stop the bullies at school from hurting all the little kids and the girls on the way home. But then, the tone all changed.

"Donald White, you have disobeyed many of my teachings, and you have never repented," He said. You and others have trained us in what to expect at this moment, and I spoke up.

"Father, I have chosen to believe that Jesus Christ came to earth and died for my sins. I am a sinner, just like everyone else, and I need Him. I was told I needed Him to navigate this very moment, Sir, and without Him, I am dead forever."

"My Son died to set you free. This is true. He has paid the price for your sins. However, all men must stand trial and give an accounting for what they have done; giving an account and paying the price are not the same thing. Too many of you have misjudged My words in your age," He said.

I knew what He meant. I was going to see the books, but I wasn't going to pay the man.

Before me, He showed all of my sins, and they passed by quickly, with no time spent dwelling on mistakes that I can't fix anymore. However, He did stop on a few of the sins that I didn't know I was making. That is the point of this letter.

"Behold the Son of God," He said, and it took me back to Jerusalem before the Romans destroyed the temple. I watched from above as the Son marched in on psalm Sunday on top of an ass. There is no way to say it other than to say it. The Son of God doesn't look like us. He had brown skin. In fact, He was closer to them stupid blacks than to us, sir.

"All of my children are equal in My eyes, and I love them all the same. Why do you still choose not to see that? Even as you waited in line, you viewed them as lesser," He asked me.

His words pierced through me as I knew what He meant. He was talking about the way we treated the colored folks.

"We needed them to help us. We thought we gave them a better life over here than the jungles of Africa," I said.

"I created Eve for Adam many years ago, and I spoke to all of you telling you that I made a helper comparable to him. What might have happened if Adam treated Eve the same way that you treat those whom I gave darker skin?" He asked.

I didn't know how to answer that. For sure, I could feel Him message my heart as I realized that "help" is a word with a divine definition; it isn't a word that man defines. People help you voluntarily. When you tell them what to do, that isn't the definition of help. That is slavery.

"You have treated your brothers and sisters like cattle that you strike when you require them to do your bidding. This is the opposite of the stewardship that I spoke to you of in my first Book. You took My words to have dominion over the world to mean dominate and manipulate My creation. This was an evil act, and you have not repented."

"I am sorry, God. We were trying to get the job done as cheaply as possible, and using the colored folks made good sense to us."

"It did much damage, and it continues to do damage when you attempt to justify it as part of your culture."

Once He spoke His last word, He waved His hand, and before me, I saw scenes from our history. I saw how Romans treated their slaves, and I saw that we were no different than they were as we judged ourselves to be worth more than them. I watched how Egyptians treated their slaves, and lastly, I watched how the Islamic people in Africa treated their slaves. I was beginning to see the patterns of history repeating themselves as we fought for freedom, not seeing that we were taking someone else's. It was tempting to start ranking them, knowing that the Islamic folks treated them the worst, but this wasn't the place for that.

"I saw what you thought. Both on earth and in heaven, happiness never shall come from comparing yourself to others. This act of comparing creates the covetousness that I spoke of throughout history. Indeed, all of you who are here before Me in this line failed to see what coveting does to My creation. You have grieved Me greatly as you sought to place yourself above your brother."

I would love to tell you what He said next or showed me, but I can't figure out how to say that, sir. What I can tell you is that Jesus Christ stepped up at the time when God was to declare His sentence, and He spoke.

"I commit to paying the price for Donald White's sins," He said. The Father looked at Him and spoke.

"Very well. It is done," He said. And with those last words, I found myself in a Colosseum unlike any I have ever seen. Every seat was occupied by warriors, not much different than me, but its size was so immense that I could not guess how many people were in there. For a moment, I wished that Kentucky boy was with me so that he could tell me.

"You can ask Me just like the boy from Kentucky," I heard. It was a familiar voice, but it sounded crystal clear for the first time in this new life or the old one. I stopped looking around and spoke out loud.

"Who is that?" I asked.

"You already knew the answer before you asked it. Feel free to speak to Me at any time. I am always here. It is because of Me that you need not cry, suffer nor feel sorrow, for I will take that from you if you only ask," he said.

"Are you the Holy Spirit?" I asked.

"Yes. It doesn't appear that you can recognize what even the unborn can see. I am with you for the rest of eternity," He said.

I took a deep breath and let Him inside my new body. He made me laugh for the first time since I arrived. I could see that everything was going to be okay now. Even though my body was new, I still had many wounds from the past the Holy Spirit began touching and healing. Just like that, I was made fresh on the inside too. The Holy Spirit then gave me a warning. I heard these sorts of signs when I was on earth, but I never took any heed to them back then. This time was different.

"You will need healing again; that is why we grow trees that hold fruit meant for healing of nations in heaven. Don't be deceived by anyone who tells you that healing is a one-time event that happens only upon arrival; healing is an ongoing process. This is why the good Lord has healing fruit growing from living trees in New Jerusalem. Healing is a part of living in heaven, not just when you show up. It is just as it is on earth.

Finally, all my focus shifted back to the Colosseum, and the Father appeared and began speaking to all of us.

"Hello, brave warriors. It fills my heart to see all of you with Me now. Your time on earth has ended, and I am pleased with the great courage you showed. Many were given guidance as to how I made them, but few listened to their warrior instinct. You have! Well done!" We all cheered and celebrated each other. No one cared what side we fought on, and that started to confuse me. Then, I looked around and saw folks from the crusades and George Washington's war all hearing the same thing I was, and it was as if we were all hearing it for the first time. General, I don't understand how time works in heaven, that is for sure.

When the Father finished, a series of words took shape in the clouds above the top of the Colosseum that spoke to all warriors in all languages. The first two filled the sky above us, and the letters were pure gold.

"Greater love has no one than this: to lay down one's life for one's friends." Then, it disappeared, and another one showed up.

"The LORD will march out like a champion, like a warrior He will stir up his zeal; with a shout, He will raise the battle cry and will triumph over His enemies."

There were more, but I don't remember all of them. Each time a new one was displayed, everyone read it out loud, clapped, and cheered. Interestingly, we all sounded a bit like the two-dozen white-sheeted folks near the throne. Sir, I found it funny how that happened.

"Blessed be the Lord, my rock, who trains my hands for war, and my fingers for battle; He is my steadfast love and my fortress, my stronghold and my deliverer, my shield and He in whom I take refuge, who subdues peoples under me." Then, another one took form in the air above us.

"But the Lord is with me as a dread warrior; therefore, my persecutors will stumble; they will not overcome me."

Lastly, this one appeared on our screen.

"The Lord is a man of war; the Lord is His name." Finally, the Lord spoke up again, and everyone could hear Him. However, while He spoke, none could speak.

"All of you men and women knew what a problem that act of killing another man would create, and all of you knew it to be a difficult yet courageous choice. While many of your family and friends failed to take the courageous step to embrace that you were created in My image, you did. You are now free to live in peace in eternity."

Once all the laughing and celebrating was passed, the man next to me spoke up. He was also dark-skinned, but I didn't seem to notice that as much now. I don't quite know how that happened either.

"I want to keep fighting. However, this time, I want to do it for Him, especially with this new body," he said. That made a lot of sense to me.

"Go ask Him for an assignment," said the Holy Spirit. The man and I looked at each other and agreed that it made good sense to do what the Holy Spirit said.

"That boy doesn't lie," said my neighbor.

"What is your name?" I asked.

"John White," he said. "I am from Delaware. Born and raised," he said.

"I am Donald White, from Richmond, Virginia," I shared, and I reached out and shook the man's hand.

"Brother?" I spoke. It just came out. I wanted to cry, but I took the Holy Spirit upon His offer, and He stepped into me and filled up the big hole that I had for people who didn't have the same skin color as me.

"Yes, sir. Always have been and always will, it seems!" said John.

"You hungry? I ain't never had a meal with a black man," I offered.

John nodded, and he put his hand on my shoulder before answering me.

"How about a meal with a brother? Can you do that, instead?" he asked.

"I reckon," I said.

John spoke up first.

"Come on, Donald. It is not like I am the one who shot you!" he said, pulling me in for a hug.

"Come on, John, let's go," I said, and we began walking out of the Colosseum. "I can't wait to introduce you to General Heth. He just won't believe it," I said.

Heaven was going to be about more than eternity for me. My brotherhood of soldiers was about to grow, and I already liked what my new brigade was looking like.

CHAPTER 6

Julie's choice to become a gardener in heaven

I considered my earthly self to be an introverted homebody of a sort. A good time for me didn't involve going somewhere or talking to a lot of different people. I have plenty of things that I love to do in my own home, and I went out only when I needed to. As you can imagine, I anticipated His judgment, including the things that I did when I was in my sphere. I thought I would hear about how I treated people at work, at family events, at church, and at home. Boy, was I wrong about that!

When the Father began revealing my life choices, I was amazed at how often judgment day focused on interactions with people outside of my comfort zone. Who would have guessed that the way I handled telemarketers who wanted to sell me an extended car warranty would be a part of the final judgment? I sure didn't. Even my choice as I spoke to the car wash assistants at Auto Bell was part of my trip into eternity. I thought the teenager who scratched my car would never impact me again after I was dead. Here is a heavenly pun for you. I was dead wrong!

At the first reveal, I chose to rebuttal; this was a trial, after all, and free will is alive and well in heaven. Little did I know that my rhetoric comments would lead to a question that would linger after my trial was over.

"God, I thought You intended me to focus on how I treated my neighbors!" I blurted out.

"Julie, I am glad that you understood the language I used, but you didn't understand the meaning. Those people on the phone and at the car wash were your neighbors," He said.

"How can they be neighbors? They were only in my life for a few moments, and then they were gone. I didn't think that amounted to earning the title of neighbor!" I said.

"Even though you treated them like disposable packaging inside a delivery box, they represented your neighbors. In other places, I spoke of them as the least of your brothers. You threw them out of your life, thinking they were unimportant. I put all of them there."

His words bit me hard. With a wave of His hand, He showed me how I dismissed solicitors, hanging up on them before in a way that I would never do in real life. I never saw that God could and did use telemarketers to refine us. The bigger lesson of that moment was that God neither laughed nor drew me into Him for healing as He did with the guy who was on trial before me. That moment unwound my fallacy that eternity is unending love. That doesn't apply until the trial is over and citizenship is granted. My daughter, please take that to heart as you ready for eternity.

The big deal at the judgment that zapped me of all my energy and blurred everything was my response to my brother's early death. No one said anything about it during the trial, but my brother's choice to drink and drive was added to my life and timeline. My first response was that the videographer got the editing wrong, but once that conclusion flashed in and out of my soul, I immediately felt a hole unlike any I had ever felt. Blame for my brother's death seemed unfair, and the Father sensed my indignance. He corrected me and also gave me clear words to ponder.

"It is not your fault that he died, little one. Instead, I have placed upon your heart consideration for your responsibility for your brother's absence with us."

"My responsibility for his absence?" I blurted out.

At that moment, the words "my brother's absence" weighed on me in a much different way than they did while I was alive. Permanent has a different meaning in eternity. I only now see that the phrase "dead and gone" on earth is an incomplete statement. Nothing is dead and gone until the Father says so, and from what I have gathered, He doesn't say so until you get to the gates of paradise and judgment starts. It required my words spoken to God on judgment day for me to see that my brother was not to be seen in eternity.

The replay God used showed that I was the only family member he had spoken to within the week leading up to his death, and I didn't know that until I reached paradise. The attendant nearest the Son looked deeply into my soul as I started to see the implication of my brother's absence. I could tell He was about to ask me a question, and the Father allowed an interruption for me to hear Him.

"How does that make you feel?" He asked me. I didn't know what to say. I shifted my focus to look at the people in attendance further from the throne. For the first time, I saw my grandmother, and we made eye contact. Based on the facial features of the people next to her, I knew that they must be family, but I could not tell who many of them were. I suspected that the grandparents I never met were there, as were perhaps great-grandparents and beyond. When I smiled back at her, I wondered how long ago all these others had died since their new bodies made them unidentifiable.

With a deep exhale, I returned to the question to give my answer. Eternity was going to be complicated.

"I guess I am not shocked," were the only words I could muster from the emptiness of the moment.

"Why didn't you tell him?" one of the attendants in all white asked me. I knew what he meant, and my heart desired to lash out. I wanted to say, "Why didn't one of you angels tell him? Since when have I ever demonstrated interest or inherent skills in evangelism?" were the words that formed, but they could not come out. I was being held by the power and depth of His question. My soul could sense the previously hidden truth that part of the blame for his absence was my choice not to share the gospel with him. This lingering sensation that I could no longer cover up came to the front of my consciousness. Instead, I asked a different question.

"Was it my fault that he rejected the gift of eternal life?"

No one answered me. However, no one spoke, either. The Son released His hold on my hand and turned me towards Him.

"You were the one he trusted the most. If you didn't tell him about Me, then who were you thinking would do it?" He asked. Until that moment, I thought the Son was present to defend me before God. It appeared that He was now part of the prosecution. I didn't know that was possible.

"I am so sorry," was all I could offer up. That was the last of the moments of judgment day that I remember. Soon thereafter, the Son presented His case to the Father, and I was found innocent and admitted. The Father could tell that I was fatigued when it was over, and He asked the Holy Spirit to begin restoring my strength. I was not "feeling it" as a resident of paradise, and God took me for a walk in His garden in what seemed like was the same moment as my judgment. I later discovered that He does this with nearly everyone.

Any description I use right now to describe the awe I felt when I took my first walk in the garden with Him is inadequate. God still has not yet given us language that expresses who He is; that remains true even in eternity. Even though He walked on my left side, I felt Him just as much on the right. The light that emanates from Him was not just warm and bright, but it was tranquil, and it pushed away wounds and experiences that interfered with our relationship, almost like the way a vacuum cleaner pulls up dust.

"I want you to see my intent when I created you." His words made sense to my soul. He could sense that my questions were about what happened after He made me. He needed to make certain I understood that those details don't matter as much as what His will for me was. He knew that my brother's absence in eternity was not the real issue. My identity was.

He waves His hand, and in all directions appeared screens that allowed me to relive moments in my life that I thought were relatively insignificant. For most of my life, I had thought that I was self-excluded from much of the "fun" events of life on earth as well as selected against, to use a term from evolution. After all, I never became a cheerleader; I was never elected to an office at school; I never became the vice president at the offices I worked at; I never had a newspaper story written about me. I had always assumed that it was my destiny to be out of the upper tiers of society.

"Now, little one, look and see how I created your life to reveal My plan for you." With a wave of His hand, I saw displayed all around me instances when people invited me to fellowship.

Jeff Gaura

I was asked to join the drama club by a pastor's daughter, and I got to see how she had prayed with her mother the night before she asked me. I watched her and her mother practice inviting me. The next day, she asked me, and I declined, thinking she was insincere. It was only now that I saw she was scared, and it was an act of great courage for her to try.

In another flash, I was given a chance to join the school ensemble band since I loved playing the guitar, but I always thought band people were uncool. The girl who asked me to join was lonely, and she had found great solace in doing what she loved with others who shared her passion at football games on Friday nights in the fall. God had told her to ask me since she had heard me play guitar in my garage and knew how good I was.

There was also a girl in my music class who volunteered at the battered women's shelter. She asked me to come with her one Saturday morning, and I was too scared to help others who had been beaten up; I thought that was someone else's job, just like it was someone else's job to tell my brother about Jesus. God then showed me how this girl had watched her father beat her mother. He intended me to befriend her and give her a safe place to share. This girl studied for history tests with me, and she trusted me. He intended for me to be the first person she ever told. I always wondered why that girl could never remember the sequence of events in history, and God showed me that He could never sequence her father's words and actions. He would tell her and her mother that he loved them only to beat them in the next breath.

"You wanted me to say yes to all of these?" I asked Him.

"I wanted you to say yes to at least one of them. That one, in turn, would help you say yes to the next one. All of these were people I decided you could help; they were not invitations to the false community, little one. What you listened to when you made your decision was not superior insight. You were listening to the enemy convincing you to avoid what might be a false intimacy," He said, reaching down and holding both of my hands. The flow of Him into me goes beyond words. All I can say was it felt like a scab was torn off, and the wound below began healing before my eyes.

Next, He showed me a replay of the invitation I got to play church softball after my husband left me, but I did not want to talk about all of my pain to people at church I didn't know well enough.

"Those women prayed over their invitation for you to join them for days." His words touched me with unfathomable intimacy, as I saw that I was meant to be socially engaged when I was hurting with a social network.

"Now that you see both who you are now and how you were made, what calling upon your heart do you wish to follow?" He asked. Just like that, it was time to pick my eternal profession. Discovery of self in heaven means action.

"Father, I think I will be a gardener up there, based on what I have seen," I offered.

I raised my hand and pointed up, wondering why I did that. After all, there was no longer anything of significance above me.

"I have watched others do that too," He said, and we both laughed.

"Yes, I will be a gardener," I said.

"Good, the process has begun. You can change your mind later if you like," He said. God's form began to blur, and I felt a righteousness form in me. It was at this moment that my new life in Eternity started.

"Very well, when the student is ready, I shall make the teacher appear," were the last words I heard from Him.

At that moment, sci-fi sort of magic happened. Either God disappeared, or I was relocated to a new part of the garden. In the distance were several snow-covered peaks, and my new vision allowed me to focus and see that there was life on the mountains, and I could see motion on the snow's surface as animals, both two and four-legged, walked. There were also shepherds, and I could see that the Holy Spirit was on their hands like mittens, and they were using the power of the Holy Spirit to care for the animals.

"I wonder if that is where the introverts like me finally end up," I asked. In heaven, words on your heart have no ability to remain internally. Before I could analyze my choice to allow them to form, I heard an answer.

"Some do. I did." The words came from my left side, near a large grove of trees that reminded me of California Redwoods but with rainbow-colored trunks that spiraled to the sky like a barbershop post.

"Hello and welcome to His garden, or welcome to one of them. I suspect you have some questions that you can't form and a few that you wish you didn't like that last one, huh?" he asked. We both laughed and greeted each other with a hug.

"Yes, sir! That is exactly my issue. Do I just need to get used to speaking what is on my heart without the ability to filter?" I asked him.

"I am not the best one to ask! However, you do get better at it the longer you are up here. Call in an eternal extension of the Refiner's Fire," he said. He then put his hand on my shoulder and looked me in the eye.

"The Father said I am to show you around until you find a place that you would like to garden and worship. He said you might find yourself drawn towards a remote section of the garden, and I was to watch for that," he said.

"Hi, my name is Julie," I offered him my name only to realize that I had not yet known what my heavenly name was.

"You can just call me Old Man. Everyone else does. Come on, let's go for a run."

A run! That sounded like a wonderful way to clean my mind after judgment day. I ran cross country in high school, and I loved it. I was good at it too. We skipped the warmup and jumped right in. My legs felt great, and I felt like I had end-of-season strength.

"You will get faster and stronger if you practice too, just like on earth! Everything we do on earth is meant to get us ready to be here, including running!" he said. I guess he heard my thoughts. We went out hard, and my heart raced as it approached what I knew to be my threshold, but the fatigue and resistance I was familiar with experiencing were not there. I felt I could keep going at that pace for the rest of the day. The next moment, the Old Man took a hard turn to the right and headed directly to the river. I slowed and stopped. Once he got within a stone's throw, he accelerated and jumped over it, landing on both feet. I stopped in my tracks and was scared to follow him.

"How did you do that?" I yelled. That would be a world-record running broad jump on earth.

"Just go hard and jump! You will make it. I have been teaching people to do this for over five thousand years!" he said.

Thousands of years? How can that be? Regardless, he seemed trustworthy, and my body seemed trustworthy, so why not?

I took a few steps back and sprinted to get my new body up to speed. When I came upon the edge of the river, I smiled. On earth, I would be overcome by fear and stopped. In heaven, that sort of fear is nowhere to be found. Although I didn't trust like I would trust stepping up a set of stairs, I found myself reaching to the Holy Spirit and felt His presence. As I lifted my left leg and pushed with my right, I heard Him.

"Trust this gift," said the Spirit. When I heard the word gift, I smiled. For the first time, I realized that my Bell's palsy was gone, and a real smile formed on my face. It inspired me; I was healed of a physical malfunction, and some sort of heavenly confidence took its place. I pushed hard and went airborne, feeling nothing but joy as I sailed across the river.

When I landed, before I could say a word, the Old Man again spoke before I could talk about what I just experienced.

"Let's go, Julie!" and with that, we ran again. No celebration time for me!

As the Old Man increased the tempo, I could sense that we were now running faster than my 10K pace, and I told him that. He smiled and looked back at me.

"Let's try pacing at your 5K time! You lead!" and with that, I took off ahead of him. The forest opened up almost at my command, and we ran on the packed dirt next to the river of life. There were soft grasses below my feet, but there were no thorns or sharp rocks to contend with. I could tell we were going faster than even my 5K time.

"You are holding a five-minute mile pace, girl!" he said. That was good enough to win the state title in the high school girls' category. All I could say was, "Thank You, God," but I didn't really know which one of the Three I was talking to. My heart was beating way above its earthly capacity.

The river was on our left as we ran, and soon, another forested section appeared. My mentor slowed down to a walk and went to the river's edge. I also slowed and looked back, and I watched him step into the current.

"Now, join me in the river but watch the current!" he said. My legs complied with his request, but again without any fear. I never looked up to make eye contact and affirm his invitation because something new convinced me that I could trust him. Soon, I stood next to him and reached into the river with both hands, and lifted up some water to my mouth. I drank without stopping to breathe. No words describe the taste of the river that came from Him. It was refreshing, unlike any sports drink on earth. My heart was still racing from my effort, and I was sweating, but before I could say a word, the Old Man spoke to me.

"The Father never said that there were no sweat or heart-racing activities in heaven, did He?" the Old Man laughed.

"But I am not thirsty!" I said, speaking words as they formed in my mind.

"Neither am I. But drinking this stuff after a hard run tastes so good!" he said, but we both took another drink of the river and let forth a deep sigh of satisfaction.

That made me pause. I had a thought.

"Why are you called the 'Old Man'?" I asked.

"Because I have been here a long time!" he said, splashing me with the water. We both began to laugh. With my question, The Son appeared, and He asked how we were doing. I could sense that my question prompted Him, and He could sense other unfiltered questions arising.

"How can old people run that fast?" I asked. The Old Man laughed loud enough to create reverberation in the valley.

"That is funny, little one. He is old, but he is not the oldest. That title goes to his son," the Son said.

With that, I broke eye contact and looked at the mountains in the distance as my mind raced. This was the unraveling of yet another mystery.

"I think she just figured it out," said the Old Man. He and the Son spoke in some special language. There must have been some inside joke that I didn't get.

My words continued to form without any guidance.

"You are Adam, of Adam and Eve fame, aren't you?" I said.

"Or infamy, depending on perspective," he said. He and the Son both laughed again, but again I didn't get it.

"But wait, are you the oldest person ever to live? How is it that he said you are not the oldest in heaven?" I asked.

"Well, there are two answers to that. I am Jesus, the Christ, and I am the oldest. Also, on a technical note, Adam's son Abel died first and was the first person to arrive up here. In fact, when you look up on the side of those snow-covered peaks, you will see him up there a lot. He trains a lot of the newcomers who have missed out on an adventure in life, and he trains them how to be explorers in heaven," said the Son.

"No kidding! You two are right; I did get all of that wrong!" I said as all of us burst into laughter.

Jesus spoke with much more colloquial language than the Father, and words seemed to form easier when He was around than either the Holy Spirit or the Father. So far, the Son has my vote as my favorite.

"So I was really confused about the timeline of earth from my school learnings vs. what is in the Bible. Tell me the truth about all that millions of years stuff. How long has it been since You arrived? Has it been a few million years?" I asked.

"Less than ten thousand earth years, if you want to know. You just asked Me one of the top ten questions!"

"What are the top ten questions?" I asked.

"Well, everyone in heaven has a celebrity status to someone else. When we meet someone who knows of us, we all get used to a similar vein of questions about what history recorded."

I nodded my head. That seemed to make sense.

"Like, what did the fruit of the tree taste like, or what did it feel like to be naked all the time, and," then Adam cut me off as he told me what was on the list.

"Adam, did you eat meat? Did you cook your food? How long had you been hanging out by the tree before you actually ate it? Yeah, I have heard it all. One time, someone told me that I didn't look anything like the pictures. I asked her who drew the pictures that she thought were so accurate, and she told me she saw them in Sunday school."

With that, all three of us laughed.

I turned to the Son, and He sensed an uncertain question forming.

"I still love you enough to die for you all over again. Speak it with confidence," He said, reaching out to me with His power in a way that I can't really explain. What I can say is that there was no difference between past, present, and future as my words formed.

"Am I making the right choice to become a gardener?" I asked.

Adam and Jesus looked at each other and smiled.

"You are pursuing that which seems to be comfortable and heavenly to you. In your defense, gardeners spend more time with the Holy Spirit than nearly anyone else here because He is the tool of the job. Every time you garden, you will experience events that you can't share with words that will feed what you have labeled as your introversion. They will also break the shell that you made on earth and cause you to seek out the company of others with a new fervor that others around you will feel. In essence, you will learn that all good gardeners long for companionship."

"Will my brokenness be on display, then? That sucks," I asked.

"Only if you want it to be. So yes, sometimes it will be on display," the Son said.

"Wait, that makes no sense to me. Why would I want judgment day to repeat itself for all of heaven to see?"

"That is a good question. I will leave you and the Old Man to sort that out," and with that, the Son disappeared.

"Welcome to the new normal, Julie. The closeness of the Trinity is something you should now understand. For now, I will give you this eternal nugget. One day, you do the same thing that I am doing for new arrivals as well. It is the way of things." Adam said.

"And what is it that you are doing with me right now?" I asked.

"Resetting you. The Father personally asked me to do this. I am taking you back to the places where you had great joy and letting His will be manifest. In essence, I am taking you back to where you didn't screw things up," he said. I turned my head as his words perplexed me. Then, another question formed.

"So is that why we went running and went a personal best effort?" I asked.

"Indeed, it was. It was when you ran on earth that you experienced longsuffering the way He intended. The other instances you suffered were all to your detriment. When you self-imposed suffering as you ran, it was to your benefit. He saw it as worship."

"Really?" I said.

"I know that there are references to no more suffering in heaven. However, longsuffering is not the same thing as suffering. You will see a lot of people running in heaven."

I needed to pause on pondering that. If we were allowed to continue to exercise free will in heaven, it seemed logical that longsuffering continued to exist. Denial of self to become a better person carries into eternity. Wow. The mysteries continued to unwind.

Adam jumped in as he saw my head nod.

"You found great joy on earth when you exercised the temple of God to take you out of your comfort zone. In fact, running was a necessary precursor for me to teach you to trust your new body to jump the river."

Part of my lack of trust came out as an unfiltered question.

"How often do you do that? I mean, how often do you convince people that they can jump the river?" I asked.

"This is not about anyone other than you. You don't need to doubt my insincerity too. I am not selling you life insurance! For now, though, feel confident with this mystery. The Father Himself took me running when I arrived in paradise. He taught me to jump that same section of the river."

I opened my mouth in wonder.

"Really?" I said. Adam laughed. He gave me a hug, and we walked in a different direction away from the river toward the edge of the nearby forest.

"Julie, it is time for you to hear some of my story that the Father did not include in His Word. When I died, I arrived a very broken man. Eve and I were evicted from that garden, and the Father blocked its entry. He reminded us again how much it hurt Him when sin entered us, and He told us twice that His intention was for that real estate you call Eden to be the home for future generations. Imagine the impact on your parents if your grandparents lost their beach home."

"People have been debating what happened for years. Yeah, they get the original sin part correct, but they miss the cause of the sin entirely." He stopped. I thought he would continue, but for some reason, he didn't.

"What was the real mistake?"

"Disobeying God happened a long time before we ever ate of the tree. God said sin entered into the world when we ate the fruit. There is a disconnect in how people understand the path that sin took. God asked Eve and me to do only two things during our time in the garden: nurture and cultivate. We didn't do that. Otherwise, we would never have found ourselves in front of that tree talking to a snake.

"We got lazy. The story you read tells that she and I ate of the forbidden tree, and that was the start of our problems. The part of the story that you don't yet know is that we visited that tree many times as we wandered around the garden during those times when we neither cultivated nor nurtured the garden, and we started hearing lies long before we took the fruit. In earthly language, we got bored. I can't count the number of times she and I walked by the tree and listened to the serpent before we actually stopped and struck up a conversation. It took numerous chats with him before we ate. It isn't the first swing of the ax that cuts down the tree. It is the last one. Trust me; we swung our ax in disobedience many times before we ate of the tree." Adam said. He let out a single exhale and stared straight ahead as he formed his next thought.

"You know what I should have done? I should have taken better care of Eve. I set a bad example for her. The Father told me later that another thing that everyone seems to get wrong. The garden isn't the only thing you are expected to cultivate and maintain. There is another item of interest that applies to. It is called your spouse. Had I taken care of my time with her and stayed close to her, we never would have walked anywhere near that tree. I still have pain thinking about that," he said.

"Wait, I thought that there was no more pain in heaven?" I asked.

"Okay, it doesn't hurt like a wound or the words of a loved one, but the memory of my error has yet to subside. That is a pain for me, but I gladly endure it. The Father says my teaching is an invaluable part of eternity, and if you can learn from my mistake, then I will gladly carry it and share it."

As I pondered the impact of what he just shared, he picked up some dirt and transformed it into water. I was in awe and spoke up.

"Will you teach me to do that?" I asked.

"Julie, you already have the power. I will teach you how to use it, but you might be able to do it without me," he said. I stood there for a moment before he continued. I think he was waiting for me to try without any more prompting, but I wasn't ready. Eternity was going to be complicated.

"In heaven, we get to see His reflection in all things. This dirt, for example, is solid and full of many forms of matter. However, when I turn it into pure water, all the anomalies and irregularities of the water are removed by a quantum field my hands generate, and all that is left is pure hydrogen and oxygen, covalently bonded at a perfectly geometric angle that the Father put in place at the dawn of time." He did it again with another handful of dirt.

"Could you do that in Eden before you two ate the fruit?" I asked.

"No! I don't know. Maybe? The truth is, we never tried." he said, and we both laughed.

"In the same way that I can change dirt into water, the Father can change our errors and mistakes into great outcomes. Had my wife and I not eaten of the fruit, time would have stood still, and the world would remain halfway through Genesis. The Son would never have come and shown His glory, and the Father would never have healed my wife and me of our slothful nature that started long before what you call original sin entered the world. I know that seems foreign to you, but no sin starts with the act of sinning. There are always precursory acts that don't get the attention, just like the fact that no one ever got fat or experienced gluttony after eating a single cookie." He laughed again as I thought about what he was trying to tell me.

"In what you call the New Testament, the Apostle Paul asked God, 'Why is it that I do what I hate?' Do you remember that? I do. Well, I asked that same question. I watched one of my sons kill the other because I didn't teach them correctly. All I needed to do was set a consistent example, but I sometimes shortchanged my gift of first fruit long before Cain imitated me. Can you imagine how that felt?"

I paused, and my senses heightened. I was able to recall, independent of Adam or the Father, the replay of what he was describing. Adam stood at the edge of his harvest, selected a lesser grade of fruit to give to God while his two young sons watched him, Cain paying more attention than Abel. My heart broke for him. Adam continued.

"I watched every one of my children, grandchildren, great-grandchildren, great-great-grandchildren look at me age as I age, knowing that none of them will ever get to experience what it was like to walk with God. Fortunately, there is a small place in the garden that Eve and I can go and return to the original Eden, but none other than she and I can see it or go there. When our mouths attempt to form words to describe it or share it with souls like you, nothing comes out."

I stepped up and hugged the Old Man, and at that moment, the Father spoke to me.

"That is how I wanted you to act on Earth. Well done, little one!" He said. I looked at Adam with a perplexed look.

"Did you hear that?"

"No. Did the Father talk to you?" he asked.

"He did, but I can't explain what just happened," I said.

"He is healing you as He shows you who you were meant to be. That is what happens when you garden; you didn't garden on earth, but if you did, you would have known that gardening is an opportunity for continuous prayer, unlike no other profession. It has more in common with music and dance than it does with engineering and science. It is too bad that your generation lost that distinction."

"Wait! I am one of your daughters, aren't I?" I said, changing conversation topics, still without the ability to filter my thoughts and words.

"Yes, you are. All of you up here are my children. Only the Father, Eve, and I can say that," he said.

"Well, that is amazing. If someone on earth told me that the first conversation in heaven with someone both in the Bible and a family member, I would not have any idea what they are talking about," I said.

"You know you could have figured that out before you got here, right?" he said, and we both laughed again.

Adam took us to a ridge on a mountain in the distance. He put his arm over my shoulder as we looked down upon paradise.

"The first step in gardening is to answer the question, 'Where to garden?' Then, I will teach you how to garden," he said. I needed to respond before we continued.

"Before we talk about that, let me tell you that I was not a gardener on earth. I worked in a marketing department at a company in Sacramento, CA. Agriculture was a part of Central

California, and there always seemed to be some sort of farming in our area that I never understood. That is what perked my interest. It wasn't a spiritual thing for me like you just described."

"To respond to your comment, plenty of us who are gardeners up here were not very good gardeners down there. I include myself in that lot!" he said, causing both of us to laugh.

"Well, I really like variety. Can I get a tract of land that has both river access, some of the stuff we ran on, as well as some shade from a nearby forest?" I asked.

"We can do that!" he said, and we returned to a place not far from where we were running earlier.

"How about here? You can practice your running and jumping skills too," he offered.

And with that, I agreed. He showed me my boundaries and taught me how to ask the Holy Spirit to provide the tools to do the job.

"Just close your eyes and open your mouth. Then, humbly ask Him to provide you what you need to do the job. Remember, He senses your attitude, and there is nothing you can do to extend a good attitude than by extended a lot of gratitude. For now, I would strongly encourage you to think about your brother each time you need a shovel or pickaxe."

"Why my brother?" I asked.

"Because you are here, and he isn't. That should create a sense of sincere gratitude. Don't you think?" he said.

I broke eye contact and looked up at the sides of the mountains with my heightened visual senses. I could see motion on the sides of the mountain, and, just for a moment, I thought about how my brother would love that place. Now, he will never get to see that place.

"That is exactly what I am talking about," he said.

"What?" I asked.

"What you did right there. You wondered what your brother might feel if he got to see the sides of the mountains, but when you returned to the reality that he would never see it, you were humble. That is what inspires the Holy Spirit to help us," he said.

"That sounds a lot like getting a bed at a hospital by shooting yourself in the foot. I don't want to think about the loss of my brother!" I said.

"You must, as that is how you learn. I promise you that if you can't learn to do it on your own, He will replace me with someone who will do something other than strongly recommend an action. Just do it. Whatever you felt on judgment day will never feel that strong again. He has already started your healing process. Each iteration will be less deep than the last one, and He will let you know when you are completely healed. I am long over the shame of being naked or getting the blame for killing the first animal," he said.

And with that, I got my first shovel. It was strong and light-weight, and it made digging up saplings very easy. I dug up at least ten of those and carried them back to my plot.

"For your first assignment, I want you to make a garden where we can hold your reception," he said.

"My reception? What do you mean?" he said.

"As you garden, think of one person who you could have or should have reached out to and plant a tree for them. Pray for the Holy Spirit to pour down on them on earth as He does in heaven. When you are done, I will come back with Eve. I will bring all of your family, both those you have met and those you have not yet met, and we can have a feast and welcome you into eternity."

"That sounds great," I said.

"I will be back once I sense that you are done. For now, though, talk to the Spirit and let Him teach you how to garden and become a gardener. You just don't know what kind of great things might happen."

CHAPTER 7

Charles "Clancy" Hamilton was born May 10, 1956. He owned and operated a small engine repair business with a business partner. He was the middle of three children and suffered from defiance like every country boy from the Unionville, NC area. His death certificate states that he died of complications from COVID on February 12, 2021, at the age of sixty-four, after spending a month and a half in the hospital. Clancy suffered from obesity and diabetes, and the doctors stopped performing dialysis on his failing kidneys days before he passed away. He was married to Melissa, and they had one daughter, Sara. Sara is engaged to be married and already laments that her father will neither be there to give her away at her wedding or be able to hold any of her babies. This is Clancy's letter to all of us. They are his last conversations while he remained alive and on earth, albeit in a different state.

For sure, I had heard about this kind of thing. I remember watching a couple of shows on the History Channel about folks who weren't doing well and how they would leave their body, wander around the hospital, and visit people. I knew that if God was allowing me to do this sort of thing, it probably meant I had flipped the calendar in the shop for the last time. The truth is, I hadn't been in the shop since early January when I was first diagnosed with COVID, and February was halfway over. I knew the end was near when I overheard the doctor tell the nurses that dialysis wasn't an option anymore. When the ladies started crying, I knew why. I used to say to people who brought me their mowers to fix that you can't expect them to last if you don't keep the oil clean. The same goes with your blood. When the doctor said no dialysis, that meant no more clean blood. I was becoming like the mowers I worked on.

It baffles me that people don't think I can still listen and understand them even though I am on a respirator. For example, I heard my wife Melissa talking to one of my sisters that she was concerned that insurance wouldn't cover the cost of a month in the ICU, and I knew we would be bankrupt again. I wanted to tell Melissa that everything would be okay, just like last time, but my tongue wouldn't comply with my brain's request to speak.

To use a fancy not-so-southern word, I prayed a lament to God. As I was talking to Him, I was interrupted. I heard a deep male voice telling me to "get up and leave." I certainly had never heard that voice before, and I never saw a white light or a giant hand reaching down to get me. I gather it was God because no one else talked when I heard it (unless you count all these darn tubes and machines plugged into me that are beeping all the time).

The only way to tell something is from God is to follow it and see what happens, right? I stood up and took steps towards the

Jeff Gaura

door, and everything felt pretty standard. My body was strong, and I could breathe independently for the first time in over a month. I felt like I was in middle school trying to do some pig riding in the backyard again. It wasn't until I had one foot in the hallway that I looked back and saw that my body was still in the bed. I put my hands on my hips and looked around. I felt great and decided that I would make the most of this final stroll on planet earth.

"All right, God, let's do this!" were the words that came from my mouth like Mexican food goes into it on a Friday night. I decided that my first stop would be down the hall to see all the nurses. Ms. Elizabeth was working, and she was Sara's favorite. I was looking for Dee, as she was my bestie. Sure enough, Dee was there, sitting in front of the computer. Who knows how many times I talked with all these ladies over the last forty-five days? I wanted to say "Thank you" for all that they had done.

I walked up to the nurse's station and put my right elbow on the counter, waiting for someone to look up. No one did, so I cut a joke. None of them laughed, which was very wrong; people are supposed to laugh at my jokes. Then it hit me. They couldn't hear me. I waved my hand in front of Dee, but she didn't flinch. She couldn't see me either. I tried to pick up one of the clipboards sitting on the counter, but I couldn't get a hold of it. I felt like Patrick Swayze in the movie *Ghost*.

"God, how many times have other people done what I am doing?" I asked. His response convinced me that this out-of-body thing was from God.

"Son, if I had a coin for each time I get asked that question, I don't know how much that would be. I am God, and I know everything! That is how many times it happens, Clancy," He said. That made me laugh for the first time in over a month. I knew that God had a sense of humor since we are all created in His image, and everyone knows I sure have a good one.

The gravity of my invisibility started settling in.

"God, am I going to get another chance?" I asked.

"You will not return to your earthly body. This moment is meant for you to see the world you called home for sixty-four years in a way that is closer to how I see it. However, you will not be able to interact with the world as I can," He said.

I had to let that settle in as well. I decided the next best thing to do was stand and listen. Standing and listening was a big part of troubleshooting problems people had with their lawnmowers and four-wheelers when they brought them to my shop, so I knew how to do that. It did not even take five minutes to see that these nurses didn't have small engine problems. They had COVID problems.

I listened to them; it dawned on me that these wonderful women talked to me more than anyone else since I was diagnosed. I was curious to see how they behaved when I wasn't with them. I was saddened to see that COVID was taking its toll on them too. My condition was acute. Their life was chronic COVID. They wanted to do their job and provide good care, but they weren't immune to all the loss. I'm one of a couple of dozen that died this month, and every one of these ladies had taken the time to get to know all of us who lost the battle in this COVID ward. They were emotionally exhausted. Two of them talked about how they had applied for other jobs that paid less but wouldn't require that they be a part of front-line COVID care. The nursing manager was applying to go back to college and become a PA. She was done dealing with the front lines too.

"Dee, you want to go check in on Clancy?" the manager asked.

"On it," she said as she walked down the hall to my room. Dee was my favorite. She laughed at my jokes, at least when I could still talk. More importantly, though, she loved Sara and Melissa. Dee could read my girls and see they were hurting every time they walked in to see me. Dee always greeted my girls with a smile, no matter what was going on with me, and I appreciated that.

As I walked with Dee down the hallway, I looked at Dee and could hear her saying something, but no words were coming from her mouth. That is when I discovered that I could read Dee's thoughts. Darn, I wish I had this superpower when I was in my old body. Finally, she spoke to herself, repeating the phrase, "I am not trained for this crap!" as she walked towards my open door. I looked a bit deeper and saw more of the story. She was upset after learning that a girl from the second shift whom she had mentored for the previous six months had gone to counseling for the trauma that comes with seeing people slowly die every day and was probably never coming back to work. Dee had spent the evening in front of her computer, wondering if she should do the same thing.

My first takeaway from this out-of-body experience was to conclude that Dee was a superhero. I shook my head and wondered how she could have that thought on her mind and yet be so kind to me. Then, my instinct to love the hurting people of the world took over. I reached my hand out to hug her, but it went right through her like I didn't exist. The sadness in her was now in me as I stayed a few steps behind her and watched her enter my room. She approached my bed and reached over to hold my dying hand, and she smiled.

"Hello, Clancy, it's Dee. I've come to check in on you, okay?" she said with the nicest of tones. She thought about saying something but didn't. So I looked inside, and it made sense why she couldn't say it.

"Clancy, you don't deserve this. I don't deserve this, and your family doesn't deserve this. Yet here we are in a room full of fancy technology, and we both know how this ends. Are you okay with all this? I am not!" She released her hold on my hand and told me that she would be back tomorrow. Then she turned and left the same way she walked in, telling herself that she was not trained for this level of chronic death.

She walked back to the nurse's station and sat back in her seat at the computer. She had nothing to report on the computer other than to log the time of her visit. My vitals were just as bad as they were two hours earlier. The head nurse told her that she could go home half an hour early and wished her a good night.

"You aren't confined to the hospital in this state," I heard God tell me. I nodded my head and made a quick decision that I was going to follow Dee home.

I followed her to the elevator as she ordered some food from her phone during her walk to the hospital parking lot. One box of Chinese takeout arrived at her condo just as she did. After she unlocked the door and walked in, she got some silverware from the kitchen and fed her cat. She set her food on the coffee table and cut on the TV. She took off her shoes and bra and started eating. She put a blanket on her lap and watched a recording of her favorite soap, with all that drama and romance that I guess she was missing in life. After a minute, her cat jumped up to sit with her. That cat reminded me of my old cat, Mr. Oliver, and I wanted to pet it.

"God, will Mr. Oliver be in heaven?" I asked.

"I make all things new. What do you think that means?" is what I heard Him say. I nodded my head. That felt good to hear.

I stared at Dee for a while. Dee acted just like Sara did at the end of her day. She scrolled through social media on her phone with one hand and ate dinner with her other, all the while watching TV. Sara used to tell me that she was unwinding at the end of a stressful day. Yeah, right. Doing three things at once is not unwinding. It wasn't just my daughter who was dumb about that.

When the show ended and the morning news came on, Dee opened an online dating app started looking at who was out there. She went to her profile, and I looked down at what it said. I nearly came out of my socks when I saw how she described herself.

"Irish girl who loves meeting new people. Loves food, wine, and yoga. Can't wait to start traveling again," it said. I wanted to grab her phone and rewrite that mess with something that might attract a good boy. I would have said something like, "I spend my time overcoming adversity and helping others do the same. I love dreaming and helping others talk about theirs. There's no such thing as too much love." That's how I would have phrased it; it's the Dee that I know. That is the Dee that a man would love. What a waste that she can't see herself the way I do. It made me wonder if that isn't how God sees her, too.

I lifted that girl up in prayer. I asked God to help her with this online thing and provide a good man for her and left it at that.

When God said I could travel, he didn't just mean physically travel. I could do a bit of time travel as well. Just like a snap of the finger, I went home with Charles, the guy who has the late-night cleaning shift. Charles is the guy who everybody walks past in the COVID ward. No patient or employee ever talks to him other than an occasional "Hello." Now, Charles and I both owned the title of Mr. Invisible.

I got on the bus with him and paid attention to him for the first time. He smiled and spoke to the bus driver. What a shame that his conversation with the driver was his first real conversation since arriving at work ten hours earlier.

"Another day in the books, Charles?" the bus driver said as we stepped onto the bus outside the hospital.

"Yes, sir, same ole, same ole. Got folks coming and going just like always. Pay is great, but the people aren't," he said.

"I hear you. Other than you, I don't see many people smiling anymore," was all the bus driver had to say before Charles took his regular seat. Charles nodded his head a lot as the bus continued its rounds through Charlotte on the early morning route back to his house.

"You know, my real name is Charles too," I said, but then I remembered that he couldn't hear me.

I was amazed at how much Charles talked to God on the ride home. At first, I thought he might pray for all the patients dying at the hospital like me. But it turns out Charles was praying for another part of God's creation that needed equal attention: the people right in front of him. He prayed for the bus driver. He prayed for Ms. Jean, who worked the early shift at the Seven-Eleven we passed. He prayed for his friend Tommy who lost his job working at the entrance to the Panthers stadium, and he prayed for the police officer directing traffic around the early morning car wreck. He made it a point to keep saying, "Take care of them," as he did his prayer rounds. I wondered why more people don't do that.

"People do pray like this all the time, Clancy," I heard. So God can read my thoughts too.

Charles and I watched the sunrise through the window out the right side of the bus. It's cold outside in February, but when the sun comes up a little after seven, no one but Charles and me seemed to see how beautiful it was. Sunrise was always my favorite, even more than sunset. Unfortunately, Charlotte traffic and all this darn attention that COVID is getting are ruining people's ability to see the morning miracle. Both Charles and I loved it. We both said, "Thank You, God," at the same time.

"Where two or more are gathered," I heard. I didn't sound like God said it, as the voice was quieter and faded out. It made me wonder who chimed in but didn't finish that quote from the Bible. I knew those words came from the book of Matthew, but it seemed odd that whoever said it didn't complete them.

After he got off the bus at his stop in the south end, it took only five minutes to walk to Charles' house. When he opened the door to his three-bedroom house, he found it just like he likes it: full of early morning activity. He was an older man, and his wife was getting their twin granddaughters, who lived with them, ready to go to school. He kissed the two girls as soon as he walked in, even before kissing his wife. Apparently, he did that every day.

"You two young ladies do well at school today, so you don't have to grow up and clean hospitals like your grampy," he said, pointing his finger at them.

"Yes, Grampy," they said in unison as his wife walked in. She kissed him and hugged him before she returned to the kitchen counter to finish making the girls' lunches. She worked down in Pineville, and she drove the family car each day. In addition, she dropped off the girls at the magnet school each morning.

"I will pick you ladies after school. Mind your teachers and do your best," said Charles as the two of them waved at him as they hurried out the door to get to school on time. Charles took a hot shower and closed all the blinds in their bedroom before going to sleep. Charles usually went right to bed but would get up in time to pick up the girls at the bus station at 2:45 every afternoon before bringing them home to help them with homework.

"Thank You, Jesus," was the last word he spoke or thought before he was out. What a good man.

I needed a bit more courage for the next visit. I decided to see my wife, Melissa. She was at the house with my younger sister, Betty. Betty was flying apart at the seams. They talked about the doctor's report that infections prevented dialysis, and my blood would eventually become too toxic to support my body. They were both shaking their heads a lot.

I sensed the Holy Spirit was there for all of us, and I asked Him, "Show yourself, Sir!" Just like that, I saw a cloud around those two women, holding them together, and I heard Him speak again.

"Where two or more are gathered in my name, so there am I also," He said. When He sat near Charles and me as we prayed on the bus ride home, He knew this event would happen, and He prepped me for the moment with that teaser. It was the Holy Spirit talking all along! All I could do was smile and nod. God was right there with my family. It felt good to see that, but I finally had the confidence to ask God some questions. Today wasn't judgment day, but I knew it was coming soon.

"God, why are You letting this COVID thing kill me?" I asked. Yes, I felt some anger, as these folks were my family; they didn't deserve this kind of suffering.

"Let me show you how you got us here," He said. God waved something that caused all the lighting in the room to change, and He took me somewhere that felt more like a dream than a real place. Throughout, the scene was guided by his voice. There were more colors than a typical dream, and I felt like a hawk as it flies over its prey before it attacks.

"I warned you about taking care of My temple many times over the years," God said. While God spoke, I flashed back in time to a time when I was in high school and my family was driving to Niagara Falls for a vacation. I sat in the back of a pick-up truck as we traveled from Union County to New York and Canada. Every stop along the way, my sisters and I would beg my parents to get us ice cream, cheeseburgers, and fries.

"You started treating your temple poorly as a child, as you filled it with sugars and processed foods. In the same way that My Son cast out the polluters of My temple, you would not let Me cast out the polluters of your temple! You have downplayed your inability to control your tongue as the true source of your current situation!" He said. I could sense that He was angry with me, but I also got a sense that He loved me. But He didn't answer my question.

"I was actually wondering how I got the virus, Sir," I asked.

"In time, I will answer you. Let me show you how you didn't get it first," He said.

With that, another scene appeared, and this one unraveled the path that I have traveled the last six months. Each time I came near a person carrying the virus, my angel would step in and redirect my way. For example, a woman who carried the virus was walking in the parking lot at Food Lion, and I passed by her, and neither of us took notice of each other as a potential risk. In another image, I watched folks sitting outside at a restaurant after church, waiting to be seated, and two of them had it, but none of us were standing very far apart. An angel guided our thoughts to get out of there before getting infected, and we quickly left to find another restaurant to eat at because we thought the wait was too long.

"My servant kept you from harm's way, and you made him work overtime by your choice not to take care of the temple of God as I commanded you to do. My servant Solomon repeatedly taught you to be wise, yet you didn't listen to those who knew more than you did. Your foolishness killed you, not the virus," He said.

Then, He showed me the big event that caused my illness. I watched as people dropped off and picked up their equipment at my shop to get fixed. I kept my hands clean before I would leave and come home, but not throughout the day. With all the air churn created by those mowers and weed eaters starting up each day, I saw how many active viruses were in the air of my shop. Nearly one in fifty of them were carriers of the virus, yet I never protected myself, even when they were near me.

"Darn! It was everywhere!" I said. I figured that working in a building with open windows and doors exempted me from all the governor's warnings and that the Fauci guy was talking about.

"Your scientists are learning as fast as they can, but it was your pride and not their lack of knowledge that prevented you from trusting them, and now people you love must pay for your actions."

He paused to let that sink in. I am intelligent and always have been, but I am not educated. So God spoke to me in a language that He knew worked for me.

"Throughout the world, people are struggling to commit. Marriages fail on all corners of the world, and the same heart that leads a man or woman to divorce is leading them to discard the teachings of your scientists. Because a small portion of their research findings was not perfect, you afforded them no grace. I think you already know that if you had gotten the vaccine, you would not be in the hospital dying now."

I had to pause this time. I had this conversation real early with some folks when I first got there. I know the vaccine doesn't prevent COVID, but it prevents hospitalization and death. Everyone I trusted told me that this vaccine was too new and I needed to wait until it was "safe" to get. Now, my family is hurting and spending time and money fixing something I could have prevented.

"What if I wore a darn mask all the time and used that cool gel crap? Would I still be healthy?"

"It is difficult to revisit the past with certainty and say what might have happened. But I will tell you that had you been more thoughtful, you would not have left your daughter alone on the altar at her wedding," He said.

"Even now, as you stare at your physical death, you fail to understand the root cause of your predicament. Did I not say in the book of Hebrews to obey your leaders and submit to them as they watch over your souls? Instead, your governor made it clear what to do, and you decided that you didn't need to submit because you didn't like wearing what you liked to call 'the darn mask.'"

As I began to speak to Him, I wondered if this sort of question and answer would have been possible if I wasn't about to die.

"God, it was hard to take care of my temple. I know You commanded us to do that, but I feel like I had it harder than everyone else. I am a person with diabetes and have A-fib. I am sure You knew that. So what was I supposed to do?"

"Diabetes was not something you were born with, nor was it something that I had planned for you. Unfortunately, your eating habits made it become a disease. Your lifetime of poor food choices has hurt others."

I never thought that food could do that to people, especially food that tasted good. But God wasn't done.

"Clancy, to put it in terms that you can best understand, you kept putting diesel fuel in your lawnmower and are now wondering why it had a hard time starting and the motor didn't last," He shared.

That worked. I thought I understood it now. This wasn't as much about the virus as it was about me.

I wondered at that moment how long I was supposed to live, so I asked Him.

"That is also a favorite question that many ask. I created you and appointed a time and a place for you, but I also gave you free will to live a life you choose. Although I am in control, you are also in control of many of the choices along the way." His answer didn't help.

"I am serious, God, and I really want to know how long I was supposed to live. Would I have died at sixty-four if I had lived a healthier life?"

God is a teacher, both on earth and in eternity. This exchange was one of His moments.

"What would those scientists you don't trust say the answer to that is?"

"They always speak in riddles, saying words like, 'probably' and 'statistically likely,' when they talk. They don't make promises, and they don't answer questions, kind of like You are doing right now!" I was pissed.

"It is good that you see that you are beginning to understand how science works. Those who love the practice of experimentation and discovery are also made in My image, just like you are. The tools that exist in their minds also came from Me, despite what the fools you listen to tell you. Their experience and wisdom have shown them through the ages that to judge an outcome that applies to all varieties of My creation as the same for everyone is bad science. They all know that radiation may kill one man in Hiroshima in one second and save another man in a cancer treatment ward after six months of exposure. Your question is below the standard that they operate. They save the most lives, even though you think that they kill the most.

"It breaks the heart at how the enemy has succeeded in getting you to cast aside the inflow of wisdom from My servants."

"Well, what happened? Why don't any of us trust them?" I asked. He laughed.

"Most people do trust them. The evidence for trusting them is everywhere throughout history. It is pride that prevents *you* from trusting them. You thought you were displaying knowledge and prudence with your wait-and-see approach to the vaccine.

Instead, you are really showing fear of what you don't understand."

God paused for a moment before He continued.

"Why did you discard My mandate to trust Me when you are afraid? What happened to My repeated teachings that you are to submit to your leaders?"

Ouch. That hurt, but it made the point.

"God, I need to let Sara know not to end up like me. She needs to take a different path than I did. She's got to hear that she needs to stop eating as she does. Please help her."

"I already have been sending people her way. My Spirit rests upon her, and He softly speaks to her when she is thoughtlessly preparing to destroy the temple. It breaks My heart when she casts aside My loving reach in the same way that you did. You know, I love her as much as I love you. And she shall have your grandson soon."

I began to cry.

"She is going to have my grandson. Tell me more!" I said.

"My gift to you is the knowledge that he is coming. The consequence of your actions will be that you don't get to meet him until both of you are in paradise with Me. I would suggest you stay friends with the janitor you followed home. After all, the three of you will share the same name."

I was Sara's hero, so I expected that she might name him after me. But now that God and I were both getting a bit real,

I took my questions a bit further and stepped into the realm of the uncertain.

"God, what is a good use of my last day, in your opinion? I am feeling terrible about what my choices have done to my family, and I want one last shot to do something before judgment day. From the bottom of my soul, I mean what I am about to ask. Can you please answer me this one time with something other than a riddle or a parable?" I asked.

"My son, all you have inquired about since I gave you this gift has been related to the virus. My gift was not meant for you to discover the bad and glaze over the good. Not every sin is a death sentence, even though this amalgamation of poor choices was. Even now, as you look at yourself during this last day, you don't see the good in you as I do. Look!"

With that, He moved me back in time to when I was first learning to ride a bicycle. Then I saw my older sister standing next to me as I pedaled it round and round. She was yelling at me to be careful, but I had pure joy and no interest in being cautious.

"You did many beautiful things with the gift of carefree living that started at that moment. It opened the door to many good things."

God showed me all the people that I had comforted with my "uncareful" heart as I reached out and loved people when they were hurting, while most would go into a shell and share only words. He showed me all the hurting people I hugged as I let my impulsive nature care for creation. Lastly, my generosity with my time and money created a place that the Holy Spirit repeatedly used, as He sent me those who were hurting and lost and just wanted a place to feel at home for a while.

"What you currently see as only bad I was able to use for good for many people. Even when you aren't alive on this earth, many people will continue to remember how you made them feel, and your choice to pour into all the lives that crossed yours has created a feeling of love that is a direct reflection of My love for you. Many people know My Son because they got to know you, Clancy Hamilton."

It felt good that He didn't view me as a total loser, even as I realized that I would be ditching my daughter by my actions.

At that moment, I watched Dee put the bowl of unfinished takeout on the coffee table and look at her phone. She opened the Bible app on her phone and typed in "perseverance," and hit enter. She looked down, and she read the screen out loud.

"Blessed is the one who perseveres under trial because, having stood the test, that person will receive the crown of life that the Lord has promised to those who love him" (James 1:12).

"God only knows that is what Clancy is doing. This sounds like something he might say. Might as well learn something from that man," she said.

"Even now, you have set an example to others. Sin was not just something you did. You were born with it. All men are. That is why you need Me, above any other reason."

I felt God smiling.

"That, and you needed someone to teach you to be funny. You may be disappointed in yourself, but I am not. It is now time," He said.

I found myself settling back into my body, and my breathing was very shallow and labored. And I heard Melissa's voice.

"Clancy, you can let go now. We are all here. We love you," she said. With that, the doctors turned off the machines keeping me alive. I felt my heart stop, and my hearing was all that remained in a functional state.

"I love you, Daddy. You know I will always carry you in my heart," was the last thing I heard before I felt Him pick me up and begin carrying me to be with all the saints.

As I began the last steps of the transition to the next life, God afforded me one more small glimpse into the future. This time, instead of walking next to Dee, I hovered in front of her on a warm late winter day. She was on St. Thomas in the Caribbean, and she was holding hands with a guy I recognized from the hospital. I think he was one of the residents in internal medicine who worked in the COVID ward for a little while. There was a strong wind, and both of them were walking barefoot on the sand towards a patch of palm trees where their friends were waiting to celebrate their engagement. They had a few moments left together before the rest of the afternoon and evening would be spent celebrating their surprise engagement.

"Dee, I can't say what it means to me that you said yes to me," he said. I looked down and saw that she was wearing a big rock on her left hand, and it made me smile. A girl like her deserved a boy like him. Well, I guess he isn't a boy if he is an MD, huh?

"John, it wasn't that hard!" she said, lifting her chin so he would lean over and kiss her again.

"Can I ask you a question?" he said. He looked down at the sand before he formed the words.

"What did you see in me that you saw that made you say yes?"

"I think it was your gentle spirit. You make everyone seem welcome. That is how I want our house to be," Dee looked at the sand, forming the answer while she spoke.

"I know we worked together, but if I hadn't seen you update your online profile, I probably would never have asked you out. When I saw that you believed that there was no such thing as too much love and hearing that you worked in a COVID ward, I fell in love with you on the spot," said John, jokingly.

"You know, I don't ever remember updating my profile with that. I wonder what made me do that," Dee said, and the two of them reverted to holding hands. John had something else to get off of his chest.

"Let me ask you another question. Is there anyone that I remind you of?" John let go of her hand and put his arm around her as she began to laugh out loud and look up at the clouds.

Jeff Gaura

"There was this one man back in the times of COVID. He had a spirit a lot like yours."

"Ugh, COVID! I hated that time," John said.

"Tell me about it! I almost quit nursing during that mess," said Dee.

"Do you remember his name?" John asked, looking tepidly at the sand as they neared a clearing in the woods. Once they entered it, every one of their friends would see them, and the celebration would begin.

"I do. It was Clancy," she said.

With that, their friends saw them approaching, and the champagne corks began to pop. Everyone hugged Dee and shook John's hand. Finally, all of them started their toasts and wishes for good luck and good fortune to the engaged couple. Once John's best friend finished his toast, John leaned over to kiss Dee with everyone watching, holding up his glass of champagne in one hand and showing off his new bride to be in his other. Under his breath before kissing her, he whispered, "To Clancy," as their friends erupted in applause as they watched their first public kiss since getting engaged.

Charles was there with his wife, and he heard her whisper Clancy's name under her breath before they kissed. After the clapping ended, Charles stepped towards Dee and asked her a question.

"Was Clancy the guy who had the daughter with the big, um?" And with that, he was interrupted by his wife hitting him in the shoulder as he made an inappropriate hand gesture.

"Charles, you stop that!" she said.

"Woman, I was talking about her voice!" he said.

"No, you weren't," said the wife.

Dee saw through the lie and let out a quick laugh before intervening.

"Yes, Charles, she was well endowed, and yes, that was Clancy," she said.

"You know, I feel like that dude is around me and is still praying for me if that makes any sense. I talked to him a few times, but he never really said much. Wonder what God is doing with him now," he said.

At that moment, I had my peace. God had gifted me with a portion of the future while I was in the present, and I liked what I saw. I also had a feeling of peace because I knew where I was going and how I was to be received. Even COVID couldn't prevent God from using me to do good for folks. This moment reiterated to me that all prayers get answered.

The only piece that was missing was a piece of my mother-in-law's pecan pie. But from what I can tell, something even better than that was about to be served on streets paved with gold in a few more breaths.

Jeff Gaura

"One last thing. Take care of my girls," as the line on the screen went flat.

"I already have, Clancy. I already have."

CHAPTER 8

Thomas Johnson's last request

In his last will and testament, Thomas specified that he wanted his will read outside with all the kids and grandkids present at his favorite place on the beach near their ocean house. Thomas had no reference to siblings or charities in his will, so it made sense that only the immediate family made the trip. The funeral was yesterday, and it was well attended by people he had known during his seventy years on earth. Still, the cemetery was empty within five minutes after the ceremony ended. Once the last of the guests were gone, his wife, their three kids, and some of the grandchildren piled in their cars and headed to the beach. One of the family's attorneys met them at the designated spot in the shade under a pier the following day, late morning. Thomas also specified that he wanted everyone to go out for a meal together at their favorite seafood restaurant once the reading was done.

The heat and humidity were heavy but not nearly as severe as the mood under the oceanside awning. The law firm Thomas and Marie used all their lives had a canopy set up about twenty feet from the outgoing tide, with chairs and cold bottled water for everyone in attendance. Next to the lawyer at the end of the folding table was Marie, his wife. Based strictly on appearances, she looked like the one who should have been buried, as the wear of caring for a dying husband had permanently fatigued her. The wrinkles on her body looked more like the rolls of surf behind all of them, with not a smooth section of skin seen anywhere on her face or arms. The family insisted that Thomas not be placed in assisted living, so Marie and her two daughters agreed to take turns caring for Thomas during the last nine months after he had his stroke. It didn't take long before both daughters found themselves skipping shifts as their own lives got in the way.

The burden of Thomas' care fell on Marie, and a part of her was glad that he finally passed. She didn't want to tell the kids that, though. She was already feeling a bit guilty. Since his death, she loved sleeping through the night without interruption. She also was grateful beyond words that she was no longer caring for a man who used to be her husband but was now wearing diapers. She looked around and shook her head. The imagery of the diapers had long since killed a part of her that should never have been killed. Several of her girlfriends who had experienced the grief of their husbands' slow death had advised that she put him in a nursing home and not let the end-of-life nursing tasks destroy her memories of him, but in her stubbornness, she decided against it. She took care of her parents when they were dying, and it only made sense that she did the same work for her husband. As she sat there, she wondered if she had done the

Jeff Gaura

right thing. Were these new memories of Thomas the ones she would keep for the rest of her days? She was numb to the answer to that question, as she knew that she wasn't far behind joining him in heaven. She had been avoiding the lump in her breast for a while now, and it was only getting worse. The kids didn't need to know that, though.

"Thank you for coming together for this reading of the last will and testament of Thomas Christopher Johnson. I can tell that he was special to each of you," said the lawyer. He wore a dark suit as his profession's expectation, and it was already soaked through to his jacket with sweat. The ocean breezes had not yet arrived, and the August morning was stiflingly hot on the Carolina coast. The lawyer's southern accent was only outdone by his attempts to charm everyone about a man he knew nothing about in the real world. All the children saw through it, but it didn't prevent either of his daughters from crying again. The phrase "last will" means that there will be no others, here or in heaven.

"Y'all get over here!" yelled Leah between her tears. She stood up to make her point as her kids ran in and out of the surf, waiting for everyone else to arrive. She had agreed to let them come a bit early to play, and she was now paying for it as their lack of reverence for this event was on full display. When she finally stood up, the rickety folding chair that the law firm had set up fell over, and she set her tissues down on the table as she bent over to pick it up.

"Sorry, Mom," said her two children as they ran to be a part of the reading. Even though Isaiah was two years younger than Thomas, they were about the same height and weight, and no one could tell who was the older one. They both were teenagers, and their acne and high energy levels gave them away.

Leah's first husband was long gone from these sorts of affairs. She had eloped and married Jose, and the two of them had two children before divorcing and calling it quits. Being a Latino male was problematic for Thomas. Leah knew it would have been worse if he were black, but a Mexican son-in-law was bad enough. At least Leah received her father's blessings when she married her second husband, as he was also a divorcee with children. He brought two kids into their new marriage as well. Leah's new husband sat next to her but didn't speak. His two children had no interest in participating in a will reading of a stepgrandfather who they didn't know, so they stayed back home with their mother.

Everyone watched as Leah's two boys took a seat after they walked under the awning. The two boys opened their water bottles and began gulping them down.

"It is so flipping hot out here!" said Thomas. The lawyer wanted to say something, but he bit his tongue and stared at the table instead. Leah could feel what he was thinking, and she had a bit of shame that he could see that these two were spoiled kids. Leah was not about to let a moment of shame pass without the requisite moment of anger commensurate with one whose last name used to be Johnson.

"Your grandfather would have done anything for you two boys, and I promise you that it wasn't his idea to die in the middle of the dog days of summer. So mind your manners until this man has done his job!" said Leah. Leah's husband put his arm over her shoulders and kissed her on the cheek, never making any eye contact with the kids who needed his discipline more than his wife needed his encouragement. For his part, the lawyer had studied the family background before the will reading, and he knew that it was doubtful that the kids and new father had an agreed-upon sense of what "mind your manners" meant. Cali was Thomas and Marie's youngest daughter, and her son Landon had sat quietly next to her throughout the display; at least one of the present grandchildren could behave.

"I can read the entire will out loud to all of you, but it might be helpful if I got the parts that mean the most," said the lawyer, judging that all the pre and post legalese would only facilitate more outbursts of the sort that no one wanted to see. So the lawyer opened his binder and pulled out the will. It was not a very long document, and he had highlighted in yellow the sections of most significant importance. There was also a sealed envelope in the binder that he set aside.

"The base will that Marie and Thomas drew up with our firm many years ago is a survivorship style will and is relatively self-explanatory. However, back in 2021, Thomas added a supplement that might take longer than the will itself to explain. First, the will reads that his wife Marie gets everything as his sole survivor if Thomas dies first. Since that is what happened, everything that either Thomas owned or was jointly owned with Marie is now legally owned exclusively by Marie."

The lawyer had done enough of these family readings to know that the impact of this "all or nothing" clause was meaningful and straightforward. Still, it also alienated children and previous spouses in a way that caused bitterness. He knew that Thomas and Marie were married, and neither of them was married previously. However, all of the children had checkered marriage and child-rearing experiences and would eventually need his firm's help with something. The people at this table represented his future customers, and he was trained to let them take their time absorbing the meaning of those words. People don't generally understand that simple does not mean easy. It just means simple. This pause to let people embrace and ask questions was a good business investment. Every attorney in the firm practiced this act with the firm's corporate psychologist before reading a will to a family.

"What kind of questions do you have about that, Marie?" he asked. He knew that it would only help everyone hear directly from the new owner what her intentions were. Nothing helps remove conflict like letting the victor speak first. Marie looked down for a moment and then looked across the table where all three adult children were sitting and spoke to them.

"Well, that is what your father and I agreed to all along. Your father wanted to make sure that I was taken care of when he was gone, and this was the best idea that we heard at the time," said Marie, making a point to make eye contact with Leah, Christopher, and Cali in order of age.

"Did Dad not want to leave anything to Miami Baptist Church? He talked about the people and the problems there more than he did about work," asked Christopher. Miami was their family church for years, and the church was always in the family prayers when they had family prayers.

The lawyer paused and looked at Marie.

"Marie, you now uniquely own the job of sorting out family priorities in matters such as these. If you would like, we can draw up a trust to make sure some of this money goes to places like Miami when you are not here," the lawyer said. No one ever hires a lawyer at a will reading, but will readings are marketing events, even though the people in attendance don't know that.

"Your father felt betrayed at that church. So when we drew up that will, we didn't attend that church, and when he died, we didn't attend that church. We were there for a season, but that is it. You have all heard your father preach that there is a season for everything, and our season at Miami is long since over. It is time to move on," said his widow. That was the first time Marie verbalized that there was a time for moving on, and now everyone knew it. The children had already talked between themselves, and they knew that their mother would have a hard time moving on, but the children knew that their mother needed to if she was going to enjoy life again. They had all watched her age as she cared for him in his final days, and they had buried their guilt over not doing their fair share.

"What other questions do you all have?" asked the lawyer. He looked at each of the children and called them by name, making eye contact long enough to hear them answer him. No one had any questions, so he continued by turning the page in his binder to the last page.

"Here is Thomas' addendum," said the lawyer as he broke the seal on the envelope. The truth is the lawyer sealed the envelope himself that morning, as all the documents were created and signed in DocuSign, and this was the only paper copy in existence. This was another part of the legal drama he was taught that established his credibility. He knew the value of what Marie was inheriting, and he knew that there was no chance in hell she would ever spend it all before she died. In addition, there were real estate transactions, accountant referrals, and future wills, all waiting to be reeled in by his subtle actions.

"To my son, I leave all of my tools and my truck, with the understanding that if his mother needs anything done, he is to do it for her." The lawyer looked up at his only son to receive an acknowledgment that he heard him and understood him.

"To my daughters, I leave each of you one of our rental properties, so you have an income stream to help you when times are tight." The lawyer handed each of them a single deed for one property and the leases for current residents. There was some other documentation, and the girls looked through it, asking the lawyer for clarification when they needed some.

"To my grandchildren, I give each of you a college savings account, meant to pay for you to get an education. I do not want you working as hard as I did to get your degree, and I also understand that college costs are now too high for a person to work and concurrently fund their way through school anymore. If you have not used all the money for higher education costs by the time you are twenty-five, it will go back to your grandmother to determine the best use for it," the lawyer said. The lawyer knew that there was zero percent chance that Marie would still be alive at that time, based on how she looked today.

"Can I buy a car with it?" asked Thomas.

"I am sorry. That is not a qualified educational expense, according to the laws that govern eligible expenses in a 529 plan," said the lawyer. But of course, the lawyer knew that there were no "laws" regarding a 529, only IRS-approved expenses and unapproved expenses. The latter has a consequence, but only to the giver, not the kids themselves; no point in bringing that up here, though.

"That sucks," said the young man.

"I know, right?" said Isaiah as he agreed with his brother. The lawyer knew better than to linger with that kind of talk. He went to the following line of the will.

"To my stepgrandchildren, I give each of you half an education. Specifically, I will pay for the last sixty credit hours you need to graduate. You need only show evidence that you have earned the first sixty hours, and the 529 will pay for the rest," the lawyer said. At the moment, Leah's new husband looked down. He felt ashamed that his children were not present and didn't know that they were receiving this gift.

Marie spoke up to help her son-in-law through the moment. She had only talked to the lawyer a few moments before the ceremony commenced, and she wasn't sure if he knew who everyone was.

"None of the stepgrandchildren are here now," she said. She knew this clause was in their addendum all along, but she didn't want to pressure Leah into forcing them to come. She had learned to keep a safe distance between Leah and her new stepchildren. Her friends had told her how self-centered stepchildren and stepgrandchildren could be, and she didn't want to say something that would make them lash out and hurt her feelings. Moreover, she was already numb to the pain of the loss of her best friend of sixty years. Fortunately, Leah's husband chimed in, taking responsibility for expressing gratitude.

"That was very kind of him. I will tell the kids about that once we get back. I won't do this over the phone, as I know how important an education meant to my father-in-law," he said.

"Landon, your grandfather left this note for you," said the lawyer, handing it to the eighteen-year-old. It was addressed, "to my first grandchild," and it wasn't sealed.

"Interestingly, your grandfather emailed that to me the day before he had his stroke," said the lawyer. Landon quickly did the math and subtracted nine months from today. His grandfather mentioned something to him at Thanksgiving last year that he had written him something. This must have been it.

"You can read that in private, as it is addressed only to you and is not considered part of the reading of the will," said the lawyer. Landon nodded his acknowledgment and moved his gaze down to the sand below the chair.

After some pleasantries, the questions about the reading and subsequent conversation ended. With that, the lawyer stood up and shook Marie's hand. She invited him to join the family for dinner, but he politely declined, saying that he needed to start driving back home as soon as he could, as he had a late afternoon meeting. The truth was he hated being in a suit at the beach and was ready to change into shorts and get out of this heat and humidity. The firm had outsourced the awning and chairs to a local party rental firm, and they had already pulled up in their truck to retrieve all the gear.

The family walked off the beach and stepped into the cars. It was only a three-minute drive to the Flamingo Grill for their all-you-can-eat seafood buffet. The family was about as predictable as could be that day, and everyone ordered the same drinks they usually do. When they were through the line and sitting down at the table, Christian and Isaiah asked Landon what was in the letter.

"Some stuff," was all he would say, even when they pushed him. When the two boys got up to get seconds, Landon looked at his mom and new stepdad and spoke to them quietly. Cali had only married Connor a few months ago when his grandfather was unable to attend the wedding.

"Mom, can I talk to you guys after lunch?" he asked.

"Is it about the letter?" she asked.

"Yes, and a lot more," he said.

When they left the restaurant, they were pleased to feel that an ocean breeze had arrived, and an afternoon at the beach was now in order. The family agreed to meet back at the pier where they held the funeral, as that was the family spot when they could get it. However, the day was sad, and no one talked about much of anything other than to complain about how windy it had become.

Once they got back into their room at the beach house, Landon handed Cali the letter, telling her to read it aloud to Connor.

"Dear Landon,

"I have waited till you are old enough to tell you a story about your mother. However, my health has been failing lately, and I wanted to play my odds and have it in writing in case I pass before you are old enough to handle the contents."

Cali paused when she read that, letting out an exhale and a smile. Then, she looked up at Landon and spoke.

"Dad could sense something was about to happen, huh? That is just like him," she said. She then continued with the letter.

"Truth be told, I didn't. It is a lie to say this is a story about your mother. It is a story about me. My dearest friends hammered into my head when I could still see them every week that context is everything. So, before I jump to the punch line, I probably need to start with something a lot closer to the story's beginning than something a lot closer to the story's truth. I am like everyone else in that I confuse a story's contents from the truth."

Cali paused again, nodding her head as she tried to take in that paradigm.

"I grew up in a household that was messed up. In the same way that your relationship with your biological father isn't normal, mine wasn't either. My dad died when I was real young, and your great uncle attempted to do a lot of the fathering that my real dad should have done. He sucked, for the most part. I am glad that your dad is in your life, and I hope you don't think that he did a poor job when you get old. My dad's absence messed up my view of some things, and the way I raised my children, specifically your mom, is one of my screw-ups.

"I raised all my children in the church. I did my best to do what God told me to do to love my neighbor and love Him, and for the most part, I felt that I did. However, all those perceptions came tumbling down one day, and it was one of the most painful events of my life. However, it was one of the greatest moments of teaching in my life, as well.

"Your grandmother came to me one morning and said she needed to tell me something. I jokingly said to her, 'What? Is Leah pregnant?' She said, 'No, but Cali is.' By now, you have probably been told, but if you haven't, your aunt Leah ran off and eloped, marrying a Latino man, going against God's teachings. I was pretty disgusted with her choice, expecting her to start making some mixed-race babies. So I was blindsided when your grandmother told me that your mother would give me my first grandbaby. After all, she is about five years younger than your aunt Leah and was not married. This hurt me, and I didn't know how to respond. I had never talked to my children about the pains I felt as a child growing up without my real dad, and the kids all knew that this revealing would hurt me. For two weeks, your mother had known that she was pregnant with you but was scared to tell me, fearing my wrath. Your mom had already talked to her sister about it, and from what I gather, I was one of the last ones in the family to know about it. That forced me to ask the question, 'Why didn't she tell me?'

"When your mom pulled up in the driveway to tell me that she was pregnant with you, she was driving the car and wearing the clothes that I bought her. I was ready to give her a sermon that you would say amounted to a Sunday school lesson on doing the right thing and dealing with consequences. I had already done the 'ready, aim' part of my thinking and was prepared to do the 'fire' part as soon as she started speaking to me. But now that you are nearly eighteen, let me say it for what it is. I was expecting to hear a whole lot of garbage as she justified herself to me.

"When she got out of the car and walked towards me, I could see that she was crying. But then, she asked me precisely one question that changed everything. She asked me if I hated her.

"I told her that she had it all wrong, and I hugged her. After that, I no longer knew how I would respond to her, and instead, I just cried.

"I never got around to telling her this, but that moment did not change my perception of her. I still loved her. I felt bad for her poor choices. What changed, though, was my perception of myself. I am sure you have heard at least a few of the messages that I have shared over the years, and I realized that I had earned a grade of F at practicing the art of grace.

"I called grace an art on purpose. My background is in science and process management. I call it art because there is no 'process' for extending grace. It is an art form that gets better the more your practice it, and you never know when you will need to use it or how much of it to use. My daughter was scared that I wouldn't love her anymore because of a choice she made.

"I wished I had done a better job of telling your mother that I would always love her no matter what, especially with my actions. I am sure that I used those words many times, but my efforts must have been the total opposite, considering that I was the last family member to know.

"My erroneous thinking continued, even after that moment with your mom. That night, when I went to bed, all I could think about was how everything for your mom would be changed for the worse. She would need to work more than ever. She just lost her opportunity to pursue and find a man with traditional means; for now, every man she would consider marrying would have to be okay with a stepson to go along with his mom. She also lost a lot of her chance to get a traditional education, now that a newborn would be in tow. My heart broke for her.

"Landon, you are my favorite grandson, probably because you are my first grandson. I have decided to do what I can to make you the last broken generation of men whose fathers didn't follow the traditional game plan. Do you know how I am doing that? I am praying, without ceasing, for your future wife. She is the lynchpin that will break the cycle.

"First off, I am praying that you keep your pants on until you are married. You have heard me talk about this, but it is God's will that you remain celibate until you are married, and at least half of that outcome is on you. Unfortunately, your mom and aunt got this wrong, and I don't want you to follow their example.

"Second, I am praying that you attend a school where men and women share the same values as they do. I want you to take the money I have set aside for you and not just pick a school but pick a school that immerses you with the Word of God and gives you the best chance of finding a wife with your values that you can spend the rest of your life with.

"Third, I am going to suggest that *you* start praying for your wife. Don't pray for a girlfriend; nowadays, you can get those things online. Pray for a wife. Men who marry and stay married; that is what this family needs for this cycle to break.

"Those are my points. There is one other piece of data to reference: I think you need to come to a feeling of peace that very few boys or men ever do. Your mother talked to your aunt when she was pregnant, and having an abortion was a possibility; otherwise, she wouldn't have brought it up, no matter what words were used. She didn't. Any time you see your mother, you need to look and see the courage that woman displayed. It took courage to come to me, and it took way more courage to commit to bearing you and raising you without a husband. She needs to be your hero because she is your hero. One day, perhaps the two of you can talk about it.

Jeff Gaura

"I love you immensely. Please be the man that breaks this mess."

Cali looked up after reading it and wiped a tear with her right hand while clutching the letter with her other hand.

"Landon, I would never have aborted you, but Daddy is telling the truth in that I thought about it," she stood there as she began lots of crying. Landon thought about the letter for one split second before he stepped forward and held his mother. While holding her, he thought about how his grandfather might have held her when he saw her break down like this.

"Mom, I am here right now, and that is what matters. Grandpa was right. You are my hero."

After another moment of tears, she pushed him away and put her hands on his shoulders. Then, since he was a few inches taller than she was, she looked up at him and spoke to him.

"No matter how harsh Daddy was, I did know that he always loved me. He always kept his family life so hidden from us that I had no idea how he would react when he heard what happened. That is really why I couldn't tell him," she said.

Cali had to work the following day, so the family packed up and began driving back home outside of Charlotte. The drive was uneventful, and Cali would occasionally tell a story from the passenger seat about her father while her husband and Landon took turns driving.

"You know, I didn't know any of that part of your dad until he died, and you read that letter out loud," Connor said. "But if I did, I still would have married you," he said. With that, Cali began crying again as they hit a wide-open expanse of highway between the beach and the city.

The walls her father used to protect her were finally gone, and she decided to adventure outward. Cali rolled down the windows and put her arm out, fully extending it.

"Daddy told me one time not to do this because the car might get too close to a tree and knock my arm off! I still wanted to do it, though," she said. After a few seconds, she closed the window. Everyone in the car laughed as she exercised her new freedom.

"So did your arm come off?" asked her husband.

"No, but now I know for myself that it won't," said Cali. Learning requires more than a teacher or some faith. There is no substitute for figuring things out on your own, no matter what her daddy said.

When they got home, Landon seemed occupied. He hadn't yet made any commitments for school in the fall. The family discussed him going to community college and getting a job part-time until he could figure out what he wanted to do, but he didn't agree to any of that. He went upstairs with the letter, and his mother told him that she would call him down for dinner. When he came down, something seemed different.

Landon took his usual seat at the table.

Jeff Gaura

"I need to talk. Grandpa's letter meant something to me. So, Mom, I got on video chat today with Liberty University admissions. They have rolling admissions, and they said I could start next week with all the other freshmen, but I need to go up there for a visit and make some commitments and sign paperwork. They have an enrollment of over a hundred thousand students, and I think that Grandpa would want me to hear a lot of messaging up there. Plus, he challenged me to break the mold of men in this family, and I won't do it at any school around here, that is for sure," he said. Everyone shook their heads in agreement at his conclusions.

"Let me play a role," said his stepfather.

"I will give you my truck and pay the insurance on it, but you can't get any traffic tickets. So you know, your mother and I were already talking about giving you my vehicle if you started at the community college, and now seems to be as good a time as any to tell you." Landon walked over and hugged his stepfather. Both of them agreed that they should have been doing that a long time ago.

"Also, I needed to break up with my girlfriend. She and I have been sexually active, and there is no way we could just be friends. I already told her on the car ride home."

Both Cali and Connor were speechless; Landon was formally serious about wanting to do things differently. The moment made Cali wonder how different her world would have been had she been so open with her family.

"Who do I talk to about all the college costs that Grandpa mentioned in his addendum?" He asked.

"I would say talk to the lawyer. He seemed nice," said Cali.

"I don't know. I am going to ask Grandma, first" he said. When dinner was over, Landon went into the living room with his stepdad. When he watched some pre-season football on TV, Landon joined a couple of social media groups for incoming first-year students and Liberty, and he started meeting some of the people who would be going to school with him. He joined the intramural football group, knowing that he would meet many people if he played football.

The next day, Landon jumped in the car and began the three-hour drive to Lynchburg, VA, to take a tour, see the school, and start meeting the people. He knew that many students would already be moving in. He planned to visit today and sign whatever paperwork he needed to, then drive home and move back up in the morning. When he got close, he called his grandmother and told her his plans.

"Did you ever read the letter Grandpa wrote me?" he asked.

"I did not. I didn't even know about it until the will reading at the beach. What did it say?" she asked. He wasn't expecting to hear that.

"It said that Grandpa wanted for me to break the bad habits of the family and get things right for the next generation."

"Oh. I thought he was never going to talk about that. Huh," said Marie. It was now even more evident to Landon that he was given a unique document if even his grandmother didn't know its contents. He smiled and flashed back to what his grandfather told.

Pray for your next wife.

"Hey Grandma, could I ask you to do something? Could you pray for me to find a wife, like a perfect one?" he said. There was a moment of silence.

"Landon, there is nothing in this world that I rather do than pray. You got it! Let me promise to you that I will do it until you tell me that you have found one." She paused for a second before she continued.

"Landon, finding a spouse is like hitting a home run. It only takes one pitch. Wait for the right pitch, but when it comes, swing with all you got, and don't be amazed at the results."

They continued with some pleasantries until Landon's car crested a hill, and he could see the football stadium and Demoss building that represented the backbone of the campus.

"Grandma, I am here! I can see the stadium and the buildings. This is exciting. This place is way bigger than the community college," said Landon with some joy in his voice.

"Well, you have fun. We are praying for you," she said, thinking he was ready to hang up.

"Grandma, don't hang up. I have a question for you. How are you going to remember Grandpa?" he asked. He let the words linger. Marie knew that she needed to answer that question but wasn't creating the answer for him as much she was for herself.

"Your grandfather was a great provider. He loved all of us, each in his way. He loved your mom," she said.

"Enough about everyone else. How are you going to remember him?" he said. He was not going to let her off the hook.

"Landon, he was my husband," she said, feeling a bit exasperated with the young man's persistence.

"Exactly. Grandma, that is what I want to know about! If I don't hear it from you, then I have no one in the family to turn to as I figure this out. What was he to you?" he pleaded. He was on speakerphone in his car, and he picked up, as he didn't want his grandmother's words to be heard by everyone as he pulled into the parking lot.

"He was a match for me. I was always a prayer warrior, full of passion for teaching and for learning. He had courage about him with his words that I seldom see. I hope you inherit that skill from him, Landon. He just wanted people to know about Jesus, and he wanted his family to be the largest part of that display of love. When your mom, aunt, and uncle fell short of what he thought was right, he was rocked like a boat in a storm. Yet he always came back, and he came back to me first. I was nothing without him. He was nothing without me," she said. Landon nodded his head in the parking lot when he realized that his grandmother had given him all that he needed to hear for now.

"Thanks, Grandma. Wish me luck!" he said, hanging up his phone and stepping out of the car. He walked towards the tent where new student orientation was starting, and he was greeted by some current students who gave him a T-shirt, a name tag with his hometown, and in some cases, a home country on it. The girl behind the table was from Texas, and she pointed him towards the football stadium.

A current student escorted each new student. Liz was a South Korean girl who was a sophomore studying to be a youth pastor and worship leader and was paired with Landon. She had almost no accent, and Landon was immediately engaged in lively conversation with her as they stood in line to get into the stadium. She introduced him to some of her friends, and they all met some new people. There were twins from California in line ahead of them, and everyone talked about the things they had in common.

After they entered, Liz took them to the part of the stadium that the band typically sits in. She told him that she was in the band during basketball season, and she loved how the team would always make a late-season run to get great seeding in the NCAA basketball tournament.

"So can I ask what brought you to Liberty?"

Landon smiled and fought as hard as he could to not cry. Hiding the past got his grandfather into all kinds of trouble emotionally, and he felt compelled to break the trend. But emotion with first words would not be a great place to start. Instead, he gave her an abridged version.

"I found out this week at my grandfather's funeral that he left me money to go to college. He gave me a letter that impacted me, and one of the points he made in the letter was to go to college at a place where you will find people who share the same values. So I picked Liberty."

He could have talked about much more, but instead, he decided to stop.

Liz spoke up after a moment to ponder what she heard.

"That is so interesting! My father and mother saved up enough money to go to school here for one year, but I needed to be successful enough to earn a full scholarship in my first year, as they could not afford to send me for a second year. I did well. They also wanted me to go to a school where our values are a part of campus life. For me, nothing is more important than starting a family and serving the Lord." The two of them made eye contact, and a connection began to form.

"I am glad I met you today, Liz," said Landon.

"Me too! God is all over this place, even in football stadiums when you don't expect it. I love that about Him," she said. Soon, a video started playing on the scoreboard, and everyone began to sit down. A video played, and it served to introduce everyone to Liberty. When it was over, a guest speaker came out. He was a former Liberty baseball player who had gone onto the majors and had made a great life. Then, as he got near the end, he said to the crowd that it only takes one pitch to hit a home run.

Landon heard his grandmother's voice in the speaker's voice. It gave him the courage he needed, and it gave him confidence that it only takes one pitch.

"Liz, let's have a coffee together tomorrow afternoon after I move in. I have a story to tell you and think you would like it," he said.

"Landon, thank you, but in my culture, we do not go out on one-on-one dates with members of the opposite sex unless both of them are serious about a marriage relationship," she said.

Courage was a discipline that was practiced, not studied.

"I understand. How about 2 p.m.?" he said.

She stared at him and allowed herself a small but hesitant smile.

"As the speaker said, it only takes one pitch to hit a home run," he said, looking her directly in the eye.

"When I show you my grandfather's letter, you will see that I am serious."

While he awaited her answer, Landon wondered how his grandfather might react if he knew that his wife was Korean. Funny how thoughts like that just happen.

They stayed up until curfew on her dorm's steps, talking about their families. When she got up to leave, he brought out his tablet and started a video chat with his grandmother. He introduced her to Liz and said that he would be going in a few minutes to drive back.

"Liz, honey, I have already been praying for you. Landon called me today, and he told me from the parking lot to pray for the people he was about to meet. You have been a part of my prayers for the day," she said. She was not about to embarrass her grandson, but she would make their family values known.

"Thank you!" said Liz. Liz appeared perplexed, but something about her countenance changed when she heard Marie's words.

Landon hung up the call and stood up to leave.

"How about two thirty at that coffee shop?" he said.

Liz took a deep breath and sat back down. It was her turn to be vulnerable.

"Landon, this afternoon before you arrived, my family and I did a video chat just as you and your grandmother did. We all agreed that I should be looking for someone with similar values, and they said that they would be praying that I meet someone today the same way your grandmother did. That isn't a coincidence." She broke eye contact and looked at the concrete steps.

"See you then," she said. Landon watched her get up, turn, and enter her dorm.

Liz walked into the coffee shop the next day with her family photo album under her arm. Landon got his grandmother to send him as many photos as she could, and he had uploaded all of them to his tablet.

He held Liz's hand as soon as they sat down, and they prayed. For her part, Liz prayed in Korean, and Landon was silent, but their prayer was apparent. They were praying for the other.

The afternoon that they got married, Landon made it a point to take Liz to his grandfather's and grandmother's grave, and he told her all about his conversations with his mom and stepdad after the funeral. He asked her to take a knee as he said a prayer of gratitude near his grandfather's earthly resting place.

"God, thank You for using this man and woman for great good in my life. Thank You that my mom had me, and I am here with my wife. In honor of my grandfather and grandmother, I thank You for the prayer warriors that lead me to meet my wife here and that I can be a father and husband that breaks this cycle in my family. Amen."

CHAPTER 9

Rape, Alzheimer's disease, and a granddaughter who understood

I was having a great day. In a memory care home, that means something. Kim is the older woman in the room next to me. For her, a great day happened when she made it to the bathroom before the staff needed to come and change her diaper. For me, a great day meant that my family was coming for a visit.

It wasn't long after breakfast when Gary and June walked in with who I thought were my youngest granddaughters. June is my firstborn. Before she arrived in my new home at Wilson Grove Senior Care, she texted me and said that her daughter was at home getting ready for her prom; she had an early morning appointment to get her hair done, but I should expect to see her and her date later that afternoon. Hopefully, I will be able to get my butt out of bed by then. Part of a great day includes getting out of this horizontal position, even if only using my walker and doing a lap around the courtyard.

Gary and his wife didn't live far from June, and her husband, John, and all of their kids were growing up the way most every kid from West Virginia grows up. I haven't lived in WV for over fifty years, and none of my kids ever resided in God's country, but I still think that the culture of Appalachia should be the standard that everyone should try to adhere to. Families are supposed to get together every weekend for fun and food, and whenever possible, that needs to include a backyard campfire. June and John never expected to have a second daughter this late in life, this late after Jenn, but I was so proud of the job they were doing raising little Christina. I had June when I was sixteen; every time I see how well-adjusted Jenn and Christina are, I wonder how all of our lives would have been different if I did not drop out of school and have June over fifty years ago.

"Hi, Maw! How are you doing?" these two girls said, and they each came over to give me a big hug. I wished that I still had the strength to sit up and hold them, but my torso wasn't strong enough to do that anymore without assistance. I turned my head and kissed each one of them instead.

"I am just fine. So you girls need to tell me how are Ms. Christina and Ms. Paige doing this afternoon? I have certainly missed all of the fine questions that they used to ask." The girls giggled and started talking to their grandmother, interrupting each other as they talked about their lives.

Gary and June were standing by the door, and Gary reached over and put his arm around his big sister, and the two of them made eye contact. They smiled and laughed. They usually act this way when my dementia is showing its ugly head, and they are trying to be polite. I just wished I knew where I was. Gary's laugh made me wonder if these two youngsters were Paige and Christina.

"Paige, go show your Maw the pictures in this book!" Gary said. He extended his right arm gesturing for her to come and get a three-ring binder from his hand. As she ran over to her dad to get the album, my mind did its little trick, and I took an unscheduled trip back in time. Once I saw Christina's hair flowing when she ran with her back to me, my ship started sailing. That little girl's hair looked just like her older sister's hair. My mind was off on an unknown journey, and Gary and June were about to get another show and tell session of mental illness.

I walked into the living room of our home. Joe had left early that morning to do something at Cary's shop, and I watched Jenn. I was making a whole lot of food for tonight's bonfire, as both of my sons and their girlfriends were coming over. My only grandchild was in the room waiting for me to come to get her. I yelled to her from the kitchen that I would be there in just a second. As I walked in, I thought it funny to see how many old photo albums she could open and how many picture frames she could take off the wall during my "just a second."

"Maw, you need to explain these pictures in this book," she said, handing me an old photo album. For sure, this was my house, but I had never seen that album, and I was curious as to what was inside of that book. Jenn had my undivided attention now. Maybe that is what she was trying for with all this acting out.

"Where did you get this, Ms. Muffin? I have never seen it before," I said. Jenn earned the title of Ms. Muffin when I caught her taking a muffin off her grandfather's plate when she learned to walk six years ago. Her second-grade teacher said she was doing a great job of "developing her curiosity." I don't agree with those public-school teachers for a second. Taking things that aren't yours should not be equated with developing curiosity.

By the look on Jenn's face, I could see that I had used an accusatory tone that I didn't mean to use. My disdain for the public schools in Charlotte shows up during moments like these.

"I'm sorry, Maw. I found it under mom's bed upstairs," she said.

"It's okay, sweetie," I said. That was my best stab at "I'm sorry" that I could come up with. My mind still wondered what could be in that album.

"Let's look at it together," I said, and I was about to pick her up and carry her with me to the rocking chair to look at it with her.

"Wait, I want you to tell me about this too," she said, as she had taken one of my diplomas off the wall above the couch. She held it with both hands over her head, like she was carrying sheetrock. She set it down next to my rocking chair and looked up at me as she lifted the photo album.

"But first, tell me about these. pictures," she said. She had a massive smile on her face, and I knew that meant she had already looked at all of them while I was in the kitchen. I took a deep breath. That meant that only one of us knew what was on the inside.

"Okay, Ms. Muffin, whatcha got?" I said. She settled down in my lap and opened the cover. She looked at the picture on the first page and pointed to the woman in the wedding dress.

"That looks like you," she said.

Oh, no. I didn't know that these pictures still existed. They shouldn't. Where did my daughter find them?

"Well, it is me," I said. She looked at me with a perplexed look. My tone must have given it away that I was feeling a bit of shame.

"Is that Papa?" she asked. I didn't want to be in this moment.

"No, it is not," I said. I pushed my lips forward a bit. I was dealing with more of this "developing curiosity" than I was ready for. However, her questions were fair ones, and I paused to take a deep breath.

"Who is it then?" she asked.

"His name is Wayne. He was my first husband," I said. There, I said it. I was married and divorced, and now my granddaughter knows it.

"What was he like?" she asked.

Crap. Where was she going with this? How do I get her to stop? I stared straight ahead for a moment before answering. Hiding the truth was one of my lead cards in life, and I wasn't sure how to use it.

"There is a story there, Ms. Muffin," I said. I felt like I was supposed to tell her the story, but how could I? I hadn't even told the whole story to my daughter. Yes, Wayne was my first boyfriend. I could say that. He was also my first lover too. I probably couldn't say that to an eight-year-old, but her mother knew that.

Wayne raped me. That memory went off in my head like a resounding gong, but just like I had done in the past, I muted it. That part of my story only Joe knew about, and there was no way I would talk about that with Jenn. *Where would I start?* I imagined the words I might use.

Jenn, I was too young and stupid to know what rape was. Instead, I decided to continue to have sex with him in the backseat of a car, trying to make the experience more pleasant for him. I learned to stop resisting. I went to Planned Parenthood to get birth control pills with my mom more than once, but the shame of that experience made me give up, and I asked Wayne to use condoms instead. That strategy resulted in me getting pregnant. Tada! That is what happened.

How did my mind go all the way there looking at a wedding photo from fifty years earlier? My mind shifted again as I went back to the family gathering when Wayne told all of our families that I was pregnant. Wayne decided that this family gathering was the best place to announce that we would get married to everyone, including me. It was the most unromantic proposal of all time. He didn't even look at me when he told his parents and mine. We never even talked about it beforehand.

Could I tell her that he beat me? Could I tell her that I fled for my life from our mobile home with her mom under my arm? I reached down and rubbed my calf. It began to twinge as I looked at that wedding photo, as my wound from when he repeatedly punched me came to the forefront of my consciousness. After all, my calf never healed.

"He was not a good man, and we split up," I said. I thought that would be enough to appease here. After hearing my own words, I decided that this was when I would cross the rainbow bridge of hiding from the truth. I needed to say more, whether her mother approved or not.

"Honey, you need to know this. Wayne used to beat me. Do you know what that means when a man beats his wife?" I asked. Putting on my teacher hat has always helped me deal with my trauma. However, changing my personality never allowed me the chance to heal from the trauma. Whatever, it worked for me.

"Does that mean he hit you with his hands and stuff?" she asked.

"Yes, and sometimes he used other objects to make me stop doing things that aggravated him," I said.

"What did he use to beat you?" she asked. *I hate Charlotte schools. I hate this second-grade teacher. Curiosity is not okay all the time.*

"He used a thick curtain rod," I said. I didn't think as I told her the unadulterated truth. All I could see was Wayne swinging the long metal pole at me, and I would raise my forearm to fend off the blows. The following day, I had to wrap my arms up so no one at work would see all of the bruising. I broke a bone for all I know, as it took many months for my arms to heal.

"Did you call the police?" she asked. I chuckled, thinking that if I had done that, perhaps he would have seen the error in his ways, and we would still be married. I had been coached enough to know that these types of fantasies are a part of mental illness, and the best way out of it is to look at the person next to you and say their name.

"Ms. Muffin… I didn't call the police, but you are a good girl to know that is what you are supposed to do." I bent over and kissed her on the head. Then, I started rocking the chair and told her more.

"No, instead, I went to work the next day, and back then, your papa worked at the retail store with me. That was before he and I got married. He told me I needed to do something, or else Wayne would probably start beating your mom next," I said.

There, I did it. I finally said something about my abuse. I knew that I would say something one day, but I never knew how to do it. As the power that abuse had over me began to dissipate, I said a quick prayer of thanks to God that I had finally spoken the truth. I took Jenn's head in my hands and kissed her again.

Jeff Gaura

"God, please do something positive with my tragedy. I am not done with my show and tell. This little girl is going to get everything. Please take care of her, so nothing like this ever happens," I said.

I rolled the sleeves of my shirt up and showed Jenn my arms.

"I had bruises all over here and here," I said, pointing down at my aged and withered arm. Joe had seen all the bruises when they were fresh. Jenn only got to see one bump that never had healed. I rolled my sleeves back down.

"Did he ever beat Mommy?" she asked.

"No," I said. The truth is that I didn't know, but she didn't need to think that ever happened.

"Did Papa beat up Wayne when he found out?" she asked.

Interesting thought.

"Vengeance is not something that we are meant to do, honey. We all have to let God take ownership of making things right when someone does us wrong," I said.

I was lying. I wanted to kill Wayne. When I told Joe about the curtain rod, he wanted to kill Wayne as well. All I knew was that I needed to believe God's word when He told us that vengeance was His. The truth is that I kept Wayne away from June by threatening to turn him in for raping me.

"Why doesn't Mommy ever talk about Wayne if that is her real daddy?" she asked.

Hmm. This might be one of the more essential questions to answer.

"Fathers are supposed to take special care of their daughters. That is what God calls them to do, Ms. Muffin. Fathers on earth are images of our Father in heaven. Just like our Father God takes care of us, so do our fathers on earth. Since Wayne didn't do that, your mommy never got to know him, and your papa adopted her as his daughter when she was about your age," I said.

The lights switched again as I began to think about my father. He didn't even come close to reflecting God in heaven. I remember stepping into the only bathroom in our mobile home and find it filled with beer cans. The washing machine and dryer were also in the bathroom, and I would have to step over piles of beer cans all around the base of the toilet just to do my business. Anytime company would come to the house, we would rush to clean up the cans, so none of the guests would be embarrassed. The sad truth is that it embarrassed my mom, and the only time she would ever address how embarrassed she felt was during company visits. Then, I came back to Jenn.

"Turn the page, honey," I said. On the next page was a picture of June with Joe. Joe was escorting her to homecoming when she was in high school, as only a girl's father could do that. June held her dad's arm, and it was apparent that she was proud to be with him.

"Is that Papa this time?" she asked. Joe was a lot smaller back then, and she had probably never seen a picture of her grandfather like that.

"Yes, ma'am. That is your grandfather," I said. I needed to make a point that Joe wasn't just her mother's father. He was also her granddad. Those are often thought of as the same thing, but in a broken family, they aren't.

She turned the page again, and there was a giant family portrait. It was a picture of me in a cap and gown at a graduation ceremony. I have attended too many of these sorts of rituals, so I needed to read the caption.

"Is that you?" she asked.

"Yes, honey, that is when I graduated with my bachelor's degree," I said.

"Bachelor's degree? Weren't you married to Papa?" she asked. It made me smile and let out a quick laugh.

"Honey, a bachelor's degree means you went to college for four years after high school. It doesn't mean you were a bachelor," I said. In the background, I heard June and Gary laughing. I must be telling this story to Christina and Paige back in the real world.

"Oh," she said. Then, she picked up the picture frame and handed it to me.

"What is this one, then? It says 'doctor' on it. Are you a doctor, Mah?" she asked me.

"I am," I said. With that comment, my emotional walls finally came tumbling down. All I could do was hug her and let the tears flow. And flow they did.

"Maw, why are you crying?" she asked me. This time, I knew I needed to give her more than a summary of the story. People in my family shortchanged me on the truth too many times to count, and that was about to stop. This was my moment to either be like the people I despise or step up to the challenge called the truth.

"Ms. Muffin, when I was pregnant with your mom, everyone in the family at that time agreed I should drop out of high school to give birth and raise her. Most everyone thought it was the right thing to do, but I disagreed with them. However, I was outvoted. When I met your grandfather, he decided that my vote counted after all, and he helped me go back to school and finish. He became a police officer, and we had a steady income and a nice house. I finished high school and got my bachelor's degree. I also got my nursing degree. Later, I went back and got my master's and doctorate," I said. I needed to pause to wipe the tears from my face and blow my nose. I could not stop telling my story, as perhaps the most important message was still yet to be said.

"None of that would have happened without your grandfather's support. He was my hero, and he stepped in to play the role that no one ever had. He and I aren't perfect, but without him, that diploma would never have happened."

"Did Papa earn a doctor too?" she asked.

I laughed once or twice.

"Your grandfather helped me. He is plenty smart, but book learning was not his specialty," I said, pulling Jenn in for another hug. I kissed the top of her head and told her I loved her.

"One day, Ms. Muffin, I want you to marry a man like your grandfather," I told her. I smiled again and looked at the ceiling in our house. There were still stains on it from the second-story bathtub overflowing last year. No one sees the stains anymore since they are not in a place where your eyes travel. Even if we were to repair the rotten sheetrock, it would still need painting. We never got around to fixing it.

In a philosophical moment, I wondered if the condition of that ceiling reflected me. I was broken from damage a long time ago, but no one ever looked at it since it was out of sight. I was now nearly forty years removed since I was raped in the backseat of an old car. And I was still in no place to say I was healed. Getting married didn't fix me, nor did having three children. Seeing that diploma reminded me that education doesn't fix sexual abuse, either. If anything, it buried it.

"I love you, Ms. Muffin," I said, rocking her back and forth.

"I love you too, Maw. That is pretty cool that you are a doctor, and you never talk it," she said. She was beginning to see that there were lots of events I didn't talk about. And she seemed to be handling them better than I could have hoped for.

Almost as if someone flipped a light switch and the room went dark, my joy with Jenn was replaced with melancholy.

I stood up as Joe walked in from work. The look on his face wasn't the same playful man that I was used to seeing when he came home from work.

"We gotta talk," he said, opening up the fridge and looking for some comfort food.

"I got shot at today. I heard the bullet fly over my head, Mae. I can't do this anymore. I can't be a cop," he said.

Once you are a trauma victim, you can immediately see when someone else is.

"Then quit," I said.

I had watched my father spend his life failing to be employed. I watched my first husband utterly fail at all things employment. Joe knew those things, and he had been a cop for me more than anyone else.

"Joe, just quit. It is okay. I make good money now. No one needs you getting killed at work, especially me," I said.

I could see through that man. He loved many things about being a cop, but most of all, he loved how it made me feel. He felt guilt that I wouldn't see him as a hero anymore if he quit.

"Joe! It is okay. We got this," I said.

The boys walked into the kitchen. Our oldest son Alex spoke up first.

"Hi, Papa. How was work?" he asked.

"Good. Tell me about school," Joe said as he deflected the situation.

"I got my report card today. It was pretty bad," he said.

"Come here, honey," I said to Alex, and I gave him a big hug. I knew what to do.

I could sense a family conversation coming up. We had already talked about home school, and this was part of what we had agreed to. If Alex can't find success in school, we come up with plan B. We got this.

Joe told the kids later that evening that he was quitting his job as a cop. Unlike me, he lets stories out when they happen. His strategy seems to be better than the one I was taught.

The lights switched again. Jenn spoke up as she turned the page to one of the last pages in the recently discovered photo album. It was a picture of June and me when I was pregnant with her uncle Gary. Gary was my last son.

"Maw, how did you get pregnant?" she asked. I was not about to tell her about the birds and the bees.

"You need to ask your mother that question," I said.

"Why won't you tell me?" she asked. That was actually her best question of the day. I certainly wasn't told enough when I was little. I looked up at the stains in the ceiling and shook my head in disgust. She would not remember to ask June. She would conclude that it wasn't that important if I wouldn't tell her about it. I changed my plan. Go.

"You know how boys and girls have different body parts between their legs?" I asked. I intentionally waited for her to speak. If there is one thing that I learned about dealing with curious kids, the one with the question needs to do most of the talking, not the one with the answer.

She looked at the book and matter-of-factually told me about the difference between male and female genitals and how they come together during coitus. She sounded like a computer. I waited to see if the lights would go on.

"Oh, that is what you and Papa did. I get it," she said. She prepared to turn the book to the last page, but I put my hand down on top.

"Promise me something, Ms. Muffin. Don't you ever let a man do that to you unless you are okay with it. You deserve better than what I got. That man should be your husband, not some guy you met at a football game or the mall!" I said.

"Okay. Sorry, Maw," she said. Oops. I must have raised my voice again.

The lights switched again.

"Maw, what are you talking about? What are you talking about penises and vaginas for? This is a picture of our dog, not Jenn!" said Christina. I could hear Gary laughing in the background. June held her hand over her eyes, and I could listen to what she said.

"Oh my God. She is talking to these kids about sex again!" she said. Gary could not stop laughing, and he howled like his old scoutmaster used to howl when his laughter made him lose all control.

Jeff Gaura

"Okay, girls. Let your grandmother get some rest before your big sister and her boyfriend come by later," he said.

"I have got to call her before she comes over," said June. I asked Gary to help me out of bed, and he took me to the bathroom. June came in and helped me get dressed and sit in my wheelchair, and the family rolled me down the hall to the breakfast area. Once I made it, they all kissed me and left.

The next light switch was unique. I no longer was mentally ill, and my body was perfect by all standards. I ran my hands down my torso and smiled. I knew where I was.

I hovered in the air above a casket and a church filled with people I knew from the hospital where I worked and our community. I could immediately tell it was my funeral that I was watching, and God imparted to me in a way that I cannot explain that two angels had escorted me back to earth to watch this part of the ceremony.

With time no longer having the same meaning that we are familiar with, God took me aside and talked to me. God and I were in the garden, and I was asking Him many questions. I wanted to know more about what happened to my father when he was growing up that made him so hard, and I wanted to know what happened in Wayne's family to make them so cruel. As God revealed the abuse that defined my family on both sides, I got a new understanding and began to feel a new peace. Before telling Him how grateful I was for learning this truth, He put His hand on my shoulder and spoke.

"Well done, my daughter, as you have discovered the freedom that comes with truth. I have decided to let you see how your courage to share the truth helped your granddaughter. Go with my servants and watch Jenn," he said.

With His last words, we returned to our position, hovering above the church congregation. Now, though, I was unseen to all but the angels, and I watched as Jenn stepped up the microphone at the pulpit. She took several typewritten pages from her folder, and she looked up, making eye contact with a few people in a crowd of many. Jenn took the time to place the pages before her to make the most beneficial as she began her tale. The focus she placed on the details of what she learned while studying communications was on display, and everyone could tell that she was a dynamic public speaker.

"Thank all of you for coming to my grandmother's funeral. Maw, as I called her, was my hero, and events such as funerals and weddings often get too caught up in feelings and not the actual events that defined the person we have come together to celebrate. I hope not that the ambiance of the moment be what you remember. I want you to remember the details of this story, and I pray you use it to find happiness and share it with others. Although Maw never found happiness the way she deserved, she certainly brought it to me. And that is part of the story I shall tell.

Jeff Gaura

"I apologize in advance for anyone who takes offense or feels harmed by what you are exposed to as I share Maw's story. When she told me this truth, it set her free. She taught me by example the power of sincere words, no matter how sharp their edge. This story has an edge to it that is a bit PG-13."

Jenn waited for the laughter to subside before she continued.

"My name is Jennifer Mullis. My grandmother called me Ms. Muffin, as I used to take things without permission when I was little, and my grandfather's muffins were one of those things I would take. My grandmother would call me Ms. Muffin when my inquisitive nature was on display. But even more importantly, she called me that when she would sincerely answer my questions.

"My first story of her came when I was eight years old. I found an old photo album my mom had underneath her bed at Maw's house. The very first photo was of Grandma and her first husband. I didn't know she *had* a first husband."

She let the crowd's laughter die down before continuing.

"I asked her many questions about him, and she answered them all. It wasn't until later that afternoon that she told me that he raped her as a young girl and didn't know how to respond. She had no friends to confide in, and her parents weren't emotionally equipped to handle it. The guy who eventually became my grandfather knew about it, but no one else, including my mother."

She allowed for a pause to let those words sink in.

"She did not let the impact of her trauma derail her chance to teach me. Indeed, she turned the table and asked me many questions in response. She wanted to know if I knew what rape was, and she asked me to tell her what I should do if I thought someone would try to do that to me. I don't remember how she asked it, nor do I remember my answer, but I could see that it took her courage to ask me. As she told me part of what happened to her as she entered into a relationship with a man who raped her, I could sense her trauma, even though I was young, as she cried as she described those events that must have happened forty years before I asked her. She could have hidden the truth from me in the same way that she hid it from herself, but she didn't."

Jenn turned the pages as she took a moment to compose herself. She would be crying already if she had not repeatedly practiced telling this speech into the bathroom mirror. She shuffled her papers and continued.

"Maw made me promise to her that I would break the cycle of ignoring the truth. She didn't know if I could handle it, but my curiosity left her little alternative. I am grateful that Maw never backed down from telling me the way things were.

"As the years passed by, she gave me greater details, as I asked for them, and she never shied away from difficult questions. I asked her why she kept the baby and didn't abort it. I asked her why she tolerated getting hit repeatedly. I asked her why she didn't try to kill her ex. Each time, she gave me an answer that I could handle, but no one else thought I could. To put it bluntly, she was the only person who knew what I could handle. So how are you in the audience doing with the truth right now? Are you handling it?"

She intentionally paused and looked at several people before continuing. She knew that this moment could pierce the souls of those who were open to it. It requires silence to achieve that result, and she left great space to work its magic.

"My second story happened a few years later. I was seventeen years old and preparing to go to my prom with a boy I was dating in high school. I promised Maw that I would come by and see her on the way to the prom, so my date tolerated a visit to a memory care facility before we headed to an evening of dancing and some subversion drinking. I told you this was going to be truthful, didn't I?"

She waited for the laughter to end before she continued.

"On my way to see her, I got a call from my mother saying that my grandmother was having one of those days. Her Alzheimer's was rearing its head, and it wasn't going back into the dog pound anytime soon," she said.

"The guy I was dating had already told me that he loved me, and I thought that meant we would be getting married. I knew that he needed to come to terms with who my grandmother was if he would be a part of the family. For my part, I was not going to be like my uncle and make fun of her condition. I told him what we were doing, and I told him about her condition so as not to alarm him.

"Before we got there, Maw texted me to tell me that she was out on the patio in a place near the edge of the concrete pad. So I asked my boyfriend to drive around to the backside of the building, so I wouldn't have to walk through the main entrance with a dress and heels on, as all the other old ladies in there would have killed me with questions and requests for selfies.

"I remember that it was early May, and the weather was perfect. I texted her that we were walking up, and she was excited to see us. As we walked towards her, she took a photo of my boyfriend and me, and she held up her hands to hug her.

"'Jenn, what have we here? Don't you two look lovely!' she said. I introduced her to my date, and she hugged him as well. As I answered all of her questions, my boyfriend politely and patiently stood next to me. There were no signs that her memory was going whacko, and she was very much engaged in our conversation. She answered my questions about how she was doing, and she told us a story of getting ready for my mother's prom that I had already heard."

She rearranged her paperwork and took that moment to compose herself, as this next section required the courage that her grandmother demonstrated was a part of a healthy life.

"What she did next changed me. She asked my boyfriend if he knew what rape was. He hesitated and looked at me. When Maw saw him do that, she reached out her hand for him to hold.

Then she asked him if he would be so kind as to help her stand up, as she wanted to look at him while he answered her. He graciously helped her up, and she grabbed the pole at the edge of the concrete to keep herself upright. She then asked him again if he knew what rape was.

"His answer worked for her, and she told him the story about how she had been raped when she was in high school. She told him that the boy who did it didn't think that he had done anything wrong. Instead, he felt that he deserved it for spending all the money and time to take her out on a date."

She turned the pages but chose not to look up at anyone.

"She told him that she didn't even know it was rape because the boy told her that he loved her. Once she finished her story, she put the words in front of him in a different way to see what his intentions might be. For my part, I hadn't told her much about him.

"'Do you love my granddaughter, young man?' she asked him. She sounded more like a father than a grandmother at that moment."

Everyone laughed again.

"I could sense that he was a bit scared of what other questions she might ask next, and he politely asked me if we could go now. I could tell what she was doing, and I needed to finish what she started. You see, she helped me screen this boy for husband material, and she let me see that it requires tough questions to see where people lack maturity. Maw wasn't done with him, though. She looked him in the eye and continued.

"'Let me tell you, young man, if you are taking her to the prom just to get inside her pants, then you better not, unless you are ready to get a girl pregnant and become a father!' she said."

She waited for the laughter to come to an end before proceeding.

"All the while, I looked at my boyfriend while she spoke, as I had heard her tell me all these things before. Until that moment, my boyfriend and I had not been sexually active other than a couple of visits to second base."

Everyone laughed again.

"I could sense that he was processing every word that she said. Just like she did with me, I copied her bluntness. As soon as we got back in the car, he turned to me and said, 'Boy, your grandmother is nuts!' I knew what that meant. He wasn't the guy for me. I needed to be honest with him, just like my grandmother had been with me.

"'Actually, I agree with everything she said. Since the topic came up, you need to know two things. First, my grandmother convinced me that I need to go to school and complete a college education. In fact, I intend to become a doctor just like she did. Secondly, there is no way I am going to have sex with you tonight. I know you have spent a lot of money trying to make tonight special for us, and I am grateful for your investment, but I will stop at having fun that includes keeping my clothing on.

Are you good with that?' I asked." She held her head high as she spoke to the crowd with the same sass that Maw might use.

Jenn looked at the crowd, not realizing that she was crying. Slowly, everyone began to clap. Soon, everyone was clapping, and her uncle Gary was the first to stand and offer her a standing ovation. She took out a tissue that she didn't intend to use but was glad she had it with her. She repeatedly said "thank you" to everyone in the church until they all sat down.

One of the angels turned to me and spoke.

"I have a message for you. The Father says, 'Well done, my good servant.'" Jenn then settled her countenance and returned to her story.

"For the rest of that night, I felt like the guy who was my boyfriend was now a friend who just happened to be a boy. He was kind to me all night, and we had had a lot of laughs at dinner with some friends. We danced, and he dropped me off at home before my curfew, kissing me goodnight. However, now that his intentions were exposed, he never asked me out on a date again." Jenn turned to the final page.

"Maw helped me understand the difference between right and wrong, not just in my words but with the behavior of men. Why? Because she got it wrong one time, and she never really healed from it. To fulfill my promise to all of you to make sure that you remember this day as a celebration, the man who proposed to me last week allowed me the grace to withhold telling all of you until this moment."

She removed the tape holding her engagement ring to the inside of her folder and slipped it on her left hand, and raised her hand for all to see.

As people began to clap, her fiancé stood up from his place between her two uncles and walked to the podium to stand next to his future bride.

"Ladies and gentlemen, meet Connor. I cannot think of a better place to tell everyone that I am getting married than at the celebration of one of the most important people to be in my life." Connor leaned over and kissed Jenn on the lips and pulled himself close to her so that whatever he said would be heard in the microphone.

"Second base, huh?" She laughed and kissed him again between her tears and laughter. Once that ended, Jenn returned to the last paragraph of her story.

"I, too, might have gotten the sequence of life events wrong had it not been for my Maw. If she was here, I know how proud she would be. But if she were here, I know how scared the guy next to me would be, as he has heard all about the questions she asks sometimes."

Her fiancé stepped to the microphone and smiled as he addressed the audience while everyone was still laughing.

"Darn straight I would be," he said, causing even the pastor to begin to laugh.

"Jenn, I love you so much," she said, as God pulled her back into eternity, as she earned her heavenly reward. She blew Jenn a

Jeff Gaura

kiss as she departed just as Jenn stepped off the pulpit to return to her seat. Gary was walking up next, and he was already laughing as he could tell he needed to change his script. As he passed her casket, he spoke loud enough for everyone to hear.

"I love you, Maw," as he settled in behind the stage.

CHAPTER 10

Down syndrome is a condition where an extra chromosome in the DNA causes metabolic imbalances. People diagnosed with this condition present with a variety of possible behaviors, all well documented. People with Down syndrome are often viewed as an anomaly among humanity with a degenerative and substandard life outcome. However, God has shown since creation that He can use all things to bring glory. Although I have never met Eric, this is his story.

God,

I love the lights. Ceiling fans are delightful, too, except when people turn them off. Their rhythm is beautiful and predictable. I am glad that You don't think it strange that I stare at them all time. I think it is weird that the other people who are also created in Your image don't enjoy them the way I do. You have several images, I think.

Staring at lights and spinning fans lets me see Your grand design. I think lights are the best thing You made on the first day of creation. Since You made them on the first day, that means light is essential. Mom showed me in the backyard garden that our food comes from light. When I hear my parents yell out, "Dinner is ready," and my sister comes to push my wheelchair to the kitchen to eat, everyone focuses on the food. I still think about the lights. I want to touch and feel the light. I watch the shadow that light makes when it hits my hands, and I want to taste the light on my fingers. That is why I put them in my mouth all the time.

I love patterns. I see more of Your arrangements in creation than everyone else does, but I don't know how to talk about it. I rock back and forth, hoping someone will see what I see or feel what I feel. The only tool I have that lets me experiment with Your patterns is my wooden blocks. I love lining them up in rows and stacking them up as high as I can. I don't want them to fall over, and I must practice correcting the build as I stack them. Dad likes watching someone hit a golf ball in a straight line even though he can't do it himself. I can achieve the same straight line that Dad wants, and I practice my craft. Maybe Dad should play more blocks with me so he can hit the golf ball straight ahead.

I figured out that people don't do what You tell them to do. I don't understand why they don't listen to You, God. I feel like I am listening to You all time.

You tell us that we are to do unto others as we wish them to do unto us. I'm not too fond of it when my dad moves the cat's chair to another spot in the room. It makes me upset, and he knows it does. Why does he keep wanting to move it? Is that spot that the chair sits bad?

You say that we are supposed to love each other. Then my mother tries to make me eat new food. She forgot that You fed

Jeff Gaura

Your people manna and dove meat for forty years, and they didn't need to try new food. I don't remember You telling stories about how they didn't have enough to eat or that their food was terrible for them. I like mac and cheese, and I like fruit salad. I don't need any other kind of food. Why does my mom keep trying to change my food when she knows it makes me upset? Is my food terrible? Why does she ignore the golden rule?

I love music. Music is a lot like light. I see the patterns of creation in music. One day, I will learn to play a musical instrument and make a joyful noise. When will You find someone who can hear that I want to play music who can teach me? The one man who came to the house to teach me piano didn't understand what a joyful noise is. He never came back once I started banging on the keys. Where did he go? When my wheelchair passes the piano, I rock extra hard, so Mom will see that I want to learn to play. She tells me to stop moving around so much.

My parents don't understand my dreams even when I try to show You what I saw when I slept last night. Last night, we all slept in front of the fireplace for family night, and I tried to talk to You in my sleep. I saw monsters, and they were scary. I knew He would save me from them if I just called upon Your name. I was excited to speak to You, but my parents held me down tell me to settle. My eyes couldn't stop moving all day. I wanted to share what happened in my dream, but they don't understand me.

I get mad when no one listens to me when I tell a story. People think that stories need to be verbal. I can use my eyes and rock back and forth and tell a great story. My mom uses words with melodies and her laptop when she teaches and tells stories to the kids at our school. That is too hard for me. Instead, I bite my fingers and make noises in my throat to get everyone's attention, but they don't understand my stories. They stare at me like I am weird, and it makes me feel alone. Instead, I play with my blocks.

Everyone seems to think we are supposed to want a career and learn more about things not in front of us. God, I see You everywhere. Looking at You takes all day. I can see You in everything. Why do I need to learn more than I already know? Dad says getting to know You is a lifetime journey. I want to keep doing that.

God, why do Mom and Dad treat me differently than my sister, Mona? They take me to watch Mona's basketball games, but I find looking at the lights much more enjoyable. People yell and scream during the game, and at halftime, the coach and the parents seem to treat the girls differently based on how well they did. I am glad that You are not that way. You love us all the time, whether we ask You or not; coaches aren't that way. I am glad You are not a coach or like one.

Why was everyone sad at Grandma's funeral? I did not understand why You decided she could not move on earth anymore; then, I realized that You were letting her come to heaven and rock back and forth with You. I am grateful that I have Down syndrome, as I think I see what heaven is without first visiting. I am glad that Grandma understands me now.

What will my funeral be like? Will I get to be like some who get to see how they touched the lives of others? No one ever tells me that I have touched them. You tell me that I touch people, but I never hear it or see it.

Perhaps when I am with You, You could introduce me to everyone else that makes the time to say nice things to strangers. I have never met those people.

I love You, God. Thank You that life is about You and Your creation. It is okay that people don't understand me. I understand You better than they do. Thank You for giving me that gift.

I really love You a lot.

Eric

ENDNOTES

1   *Jenny*: rifle.

2   *Flash in the pan:* When the powder only partially ignites but lacks the force to expel a bullet. A bright light is observed, but no shot is fired.

3   *Meat wagon:* cart used on the battlefield to carry off wounded soldiers to the medical tent.

4   *Horse sense:* common sense.

5   *Acknowledge the corn:* see the truth.

6   *Pog:* Person Other than a Grunt.

7   *Jeep:* soldier just out of basic training.

8   *Joe:* soldier.

9   *Sleeve:* soldier with no rank or awards.

10   *Head:* bathroom.

11   *Rack:* bed.

12   *Fugazi:* slang to describe a situation that is screwed up.

13   *Hospital rats:* someone who fakes illness to get out of duty.

9 781637 697825